DRAWINGS BY DEGAS

DRAWINGS BY DEGAS

ESSAY AND CATALOGUE BY JEAN SUTHERLAND BOGGS

CITY ART MUSEUM OF SAINT LOUIS

PHILADELPHIA MUSEUM OF ART

THE MINNEAPOLIS SOCIETY OF FINE ARTS

DISTRIBUTED BY HARRY N. ABRAMS, INC.

PARTICIPATING MUSEUMS

City Art Museum of Saint Louis

Philadelphia Museum of Art

If on several occasions in the recent past we have seen important exhibitions in this country of work by the great French master, Edgar Hilaire Germain Degas, now have we our first opportunity to consider upwards of one hundred and fifty of his drawings representing virtually every stage in the evolution of a long and productive life devoted entirely to art. Through *Drawings by Degas* the art museums of St. Louis, Philadelphia and Minneapolis pay tribute to the graphic side of Degas's genius. Moreover, it is appropriate that we should do this in 1967, the year that marks the fiftieth of his death.

For the exceptional opportunity that museum visitors in these three cities have to reflect on Degas as a draftsman we are beholden to a long list of owners whom we are pleased to recognize by name elsewhere in this catalogue. These lenders have most graciously consented to giving up their drawings for an extended period of time so that we, too, might experience the pleasure they afford in their home surroundings. With surprisingly few exceptions our requests for loans were granted. Indeed, we were refused only when owners informed us, quite rightly, that it would be courting too great a risk if they were to permit certain especially fragile drawings to travel. It seemed almost as though everyone who possessed a drawing by Degas was in accord with the aim of an exhibition devoted to his graphic style and was therefore eager to be helpful. Although the problem of sending works of art to *Drawings by Degas* understandably presents somewhat more complex problems for European collectors and museums than for those at home, they responded no less willingly. Because of these European loans the exhibition is all the richer by having included in it several major drawings which have never been shown this side of the Atlantic.

Dr. Jean Sutherland Boggs, who became Director of The National Gallery of Canada in June of this year, and who from the start of our planning has been architect-in-chief of the exhibition, reminds us once more of the true stature of Edgar Degas. She has done this brilliantly through her choice of drawings which represents the full range of the artist's approach to a many-sided but, after all, essentially Parisian world. From the breathtakingly beautiful fans to the powerful and even brutally conceived bathers of the 1890's, Miss Boggs demonstrates the evolution of Degas the draftsman showing us how he was ever striving to bring vividly to life subject matter which few of his contemporaries had the courage to explore. Owing to this lasting struggle to give form to his vision, Degas's final drawings achieve a grandeur that is not to be found in his more precise but surely no less beautiful style of the 1870's. Seen as a whole this exhibition offers not only visual stimulation in abundance but deepens our insight into the artist himself whom we see perennially as one of the most extraordinary, creative figures of his time. Even though 1967 marks the half century of his death we recognize that as time passes this was only yesterday; yet how right we are to think of Degas as being a timeless figure, at home in the company of all great draftsmen.

Work on the exhibition began when Miss Boggs was still Steinberg Professor of the History of Art at Washington University, St. Louis. Despite her demanding teaching schedule she found time to work closely with the staff of City Art

Museum in formulating and carrying out plans. The Trustees and Director of City Art Museum wish to express their gratitude to Washington University, the Steinberg Foundation and to the distinguished museum over which Miss Boggs now presides for granting her time to work on the exhibition.

Miss Boggs and the staff of City Art Museum were assisted by many museum directors, curators, scholars, art dealers, private collectors and librarians who furnished information and were helpful in numerous practical ways in making our task easier. Miss Pamela Osler of The National Gallery of Canada and Miss Martha Baer of City Art Museum gave faithful and expert attention to the many organizational details of this exhibition and the preparation of the catalogue. Miss Emily S. Rauh, Curator of City Art Museum, assisted in the preliminary selection of drawings and helped the exhibition to take form in many other ways. Mr. Richard S. Cleveland, Registrar and Assistant Curator of Oriental Art of City Art Museum, dealt with the many details having to do with the loan and transportation of the drawings. Special thanks, however, must go to the following for the close personal interest they have shown in the preparation of the exhibition: Jacob Bean, Curator of Drawings, The Metropolitan Museum of Art; M. and Mme. Georges Bernier, Paris; David Carritt, Christie, Manson & Woods Ltd.; Bruce Chatwin, Sotheby & Company; Ralph T. Coe, Assistant Director, William Rockhill Nelson Gallery of Art—Atkins Museum of Fine Arts; Douglas Cooper, Argilliers; Charles Durand-Ruel, Durand-Ruel & Company, Paris; William N. Eisendrath, Jr., Curator of the Collections, Steinberg Hall, Washington University; Mrs. Marianne Feilchenfeldt, Zurich; Henry G. Gardiner, Assistant Curator of Painting, Philadelphia Museum of Art; Louis Goldenberg, Wildenstein & Company, Inc., New York; L. J. Herrmann, Assistant Keeper of the Department of Western Art, Ashmolean Museum, Oxford University; H. R. Hoetnik, Curator of Drawings, Museum Boymans-van Beuningen; William Ittman, Washington University; Harold Joachim, Curator of Prints and Drawings, The Art Institute of Chicago; Frits Lugt, Institut Néerlandais, Paris; Mrs. Stephanie Maison, Faerber and Maison Limited, London; Miss Agnes Mongan, Assistant Director and Curator of Drawings, Fogg Art Museum, Harvard University; Mme. Geneviève Monnier, Cabinet des Dessins, Musée du Louvre; Peter Nathan, Zurich; François Perot, Conservateur-adjoint, Petit Palais, Paris; Mrs. Joseph Pulitzer, Jr., St. Louis; Helmut Ripperger, M. Knoedler & Company, New York; Daniel Robbins, Director, Museum of Art, Rhode Island School of Design; Norman Rudin, Yale University; Miss Eleanor A. Sayre, Assistant Curator of Prints, Museum of Fine Arts, Boston; Maurice Sérullaz, Conservateur du Cabinet des Dessins, Musée du Louvre; Mr. and Mrs. Charles E. Slatkin, New York; Alexandre Rosenberg, Paul Rosenberg & Company, New York; Gunter Thiem, Hauptkonservator, Graphische Sammlung, Staatsgalerie Stuttgart; Hans-Günter Wachtmann, Von der Heydt Museum, and Ellis Waterhouse, Director, The Barber Institute of Fine Arts, Birmingham University.

CHARLES E. BUCKLEY, *Director City Art Museum of Saint Louis*

LENDERS

DR. HERMANN J. ABS

GIANNI AGNELLI

ALLEN MEMORIAL ART MUSEUM,
    OBERLIN COLLEGE

ART ASSOCIATION OF INDIANAPOLIS,
    HERRON MUSEUM OF ART

THE ART INSTITUTE OF CHICAGO

ASHMOLEAN MUSEUM

THE JOAN AND LESTER AVNET COLLECTION

WALTER C. BAKER

THE BALTIMORE MUSEUM OF ART

THE BARBER INSTITUTE OF FINE ARTS,
    BIRMINGHAM UNIVERSITY

ELMER BELT LIBRARY OF VINCIANA,
    UNIVERSITY OF CALIFORNIA, LOS ANGELES

COLONEL SAMUEL A. BERGER

MRS. ALDO B. BERTOZZI

MRS. A. K. M. BOERLAGE-KOENIGS

PAUL BRAME

THEODORA W. BROWN

JOHN BRYSON

BARON LOUIS DE CHOLLET

CINNCINATI ART MUSEUM

THE CLEVELAND MUSEUM OF ART

STEPHEN R. CURRIER

DAVID DANIELS

ISAAC DELGADO MUSEUM OF ART

THE DETROIT INSTITUTE OF ARTS

MR. AND MRS. R. E. A. DREY

CHARLES DURAND-RUEL

MR. AND MRS. MICHAEL H. EGNAL

THE EVERGREEN HOUSE FOUNDATION

MRS. MARIANNE FEILCHENFELDT

FOGG ART MUSEUM, HARVARD UNIVERSITY

MRS. MURIEL BULTMAN FRANCIS

GUILLAUME GUERIN

BARONESS ALAIN DE GUNZBURG

MR. AND MRS. NATHAN L. HALPERN

OVETA CULP HOBBY

MR. AND MRS. ELIOT HODGKIN

JOHN G. JOHNSON COLLECTION

MRS. WERNER E. JOSTEN

MRS. SIEGFRIED KRAMARSKY

HERMAN H. LEVY, O. B. E.

MR. AND MRS. ALEX M. LEWYT

MR. AND MRS. W. HILDING LINDBERG

MR. AND MRS. JOSHUA LOGAN

CONTENTS

EDGAR DEGAS AND DRAWING

Drawing was for Edgar Degas, as it has been for most artists, the first reaction, the initial response to an idea or, more often, to something seen. Although he was a painter, print-maker and sculptor as well, his drawings are the most intimate and spontaneous reflection of the still rather reserved personality of Edgar Degas. He did not, however, consider them casual productions. As a collector of drawings himself who was particularly proud of his 33 by Ingres, 56 by Delacroix, and 12 by Manet, he thought of a drawing as something to be prized, framed and even hung on a wall. Upon occasions he would give one of his own to a friend, writing a dedication on it with considerable formality. One of these (no. 75) in the exhibition is dedicated to Théodore Duret, a discriminating critic, collector and writer.

In the drawings we can see the traditionalist and the revolutionary in Edgar Degas, never quite in conflict, never quite reconciled, but living together in the tension all his drawings reveal. This combination is not surprising considering the background of his family which was more unconventional and adventuresome than the usual biographical accounts indicate. His mother's father was a Creole born in Haiti who immigrated to New Orleans, maintained connections with France where his children were educated, and died hunting silver in Mexico. His father's father had escaped from France during the Revolution and had established himself as a prosperous banker in Naples against all odds. Although the Parisian household of Degas's Neapolitan-born father and New Orleans-born mother might have seemed respectably bourgeois and conventionally French, it did have horizons beyond Paris itself. When the painter died he still owned property in Naples, and years after his death, the descendants of his younger brother René were disputing the settlement of the painter's estate from Paris and New Orleans. The image of the Parisian Degas, although convincing, is incomplete. Again, in his personal life there was often a tension between convention and actuality.

When Degas began to draw, he did so with a respect for the past. Our first record of him as an artist is copying paintings in the Louvre and prints at the Bibliothèque Nationale. His early notebooks show the student timidly trying to record what he had seen in life and in works of art. What training he had as an artist, a period with Lamothe, a few months at most at the Ecole des Beaux-Arts, some years of self-education in Italy, made him more confident but did nothing to destroy his humility before the great works and great traditions of the past. In this period of apprenticeship, which lasted essentially until he was thirty in 1864, Degas copied constantly but copied in a far greater range than that suggested by the academic discipline. He not only paid homage to the Renaissance and Classical antiquity and moved back and forth between those two poles in the French tradition which were represented by Rubens and Poussin in the seventeenth-century and by Delacroix and Ingres in the nineteenth, but he went further afield, as Professor Reff has shown in the *Burlington Magazine*, into the art of Egypt and the Near East. His other drawings were usually studies for works within the conventional pattern of French Salon painting; there were, of course, also academic studies from the nude.

Within the restrictions of the subjects of his early drawings Degas revealed a probing, if not yet adventurous, spirit. What does come across most obviously in the portraits, and even in the copies and sketches for historical works, is a concern for the psychology of the human being, particularly the human being in a dramatic moment. Whether he sketched himself (no. 1) or made a drawing from Filippino Lippi's *Self Portrait (no. 18)* he was still aware of the tensions and hesitations which exist behind the face's mask. Whether he copied the head of the *Virgin of the Rocks* (no. 19) by Leonardo or drew the archer for his own *Malheurs de la Ville d'Orleans* (no. 40), he was conscious of human response to events beyond human control. Even when he sketched in life classes in Rome (nos. 7 to 12) he could never subdue his interest in personality and in dramatic possibilities to a point where his academic nudes would possess a traditional classical calm. This sense of human drama, still somewhat hesitantly realized in pencil, occasionally touched with color, lies just below the surface of his early works.

When Degas entered a period of independent activity in the 1860s, more consistent with the adventurous spirit of his grandfathers, he did so with a sense of camaraderie with painter friends like Manet, Fantin-Latour, Whistler, Arthur Stevens and James Tissot. It was a period in which these artists were preoccupied with the reality of the external world and were strongly influenced by Courbet and photography. Their painting tended towards genre and often the anecdotal. Degas was affected by all of this, as his drawings reveal, but was saved from the superficiality of the work of Tissot and Stevens because of a certain inherent realism and perhaps by a fundamental lack of physical sensuality which never permitted him to indulge in the distractions of silken textures of linear arabesques. His preliminary drawings, for example the sketch of the *Wounded Jockey* (no. 45), have a harshness and angularity which still exists underneath the more finished works like the Chicago gouache of *Four Jockeys* (no. 46). In this masterly drawing there is again that tension between tradition and creation. The repetition of the single figure four times suggests the methods of draughtsmen like Watteau in the eighteenth century; and Watteau himself would have enjoyed the nicety and harmony with which Degas composed the jockeys on the page. The contemporary subject is part of the convention of the world in which Degas lived. At the same time the adventurous, creative side of the painter is shown in the unconventional view of the jockeys themselves; and it was often in the angle or point of view that Degas's originality was revealed. He was also becoming more suave and more daring in the use of media, combining oil paint, gouache, pastel, ink, pencil and charcoal as he desired.

With the first Impressionist exhibition in 1874, when Degas was forty, he could be said to have entered into another phase of his development and one which we are apt to associate, not too illogically, with the ballet. Although we know Degas was struggling with certain family humiliations, including possible bankruptcy, the image of him which emerges is that of the independent and urbane theatre-going artist, caustic and sophisticated, tempering his realism with an ironic humor. His work assumed an even greater spontaneity than it had in the past. In a drawing like that of *Miss Cassatt in the Louvre* (no. 85), there is an intensification of the interest in the unexpected point of view, which he had already revealed in the sixties but which was now sharpened by a wit which arises out of the expressive and slightly exaggerated movements of the human body and from the surprising juxtapositions of human personalities. Here, one might claim that only the adventurous side of Degas revealed itself, but like all of Degas's work in the seventies, there is a reflection of another tradition which he had come to respect: this was Japanese painting and print-making. The tension is now between his fundamentally European realism, which makes him conscious even of the wrinkles in the two women's dresses, and the Japanese feeling for simplified decorative pattern. Although the general effect of his drawings is highly assured, the strokes of his pencil and of his brush are often curiously repetitive and, if they should be moved from their descriptive roles, would seem somewhat gauche. But Degas's line was never ornamental, and his drawing never decorative. It was, as he himself said, "a way of seeing form,"—an exploration, searching, rather than the imposition of even an ideally beautiful convention.

As he moved out of the seventies Degas's work became increasingly free, and he depended more upon charcoal and pastel than upon ink, pencil and gouache. His drawings became larger and more open in their impression, in keeping with his more generous feeling towards the subjects themselves. It was in the eighties that he made his remarkable studies of nudes which have a force and warmth his work had not possessed before. The sense of human drama which Degas had revealed from his first hesitant drawings assumed a different character than it had in the seventies; it was not a witty comedy of manners but began to express, through the forceful light and shade of the charcoal and pastel, deeper and more passionate human emotions.

The works of Degas's last years are naked exposures of the artist's own tribulations. His eyesight was suffering and would eventually take him close to total blindness. He worked on an increasingly large scale, frequently tracing another drawing on to tracing paper or making a counter-proof of a charcoal which he would later develop into pastel. He used his sticks of charcoal and pastel vigorously, applying them to the paper with enormous boldness, but revealing inevitably his own irritations and frustrations. These drawings often seem the most moving to twentieth-century eyes because they express the anxieties which have troubled our century most. In them we do not feel so much the tension between Degas the traditionalist and Degas the adventurer, but the anger and the heroism with which Degas struggled as he gave up the standards of the past. In the final drawings the adventurer became the tragic victor.

JEAN SUTHERLAND BOGGS

CATALOGUE

1 SELF-PORTRAIT 1855

ATELIER stamp l.l.
Study for LEMOISNE 3-5
Sanguine
11⅝ x 8½ in. (29.5 x 21.5 cm.)
*Provenance: Vente Succession de René de
Gas,* Hotel Drouot, Paris, November 10,
1927, no. 12
Exhibitions: Providence 1931; Buffalo 1935,
no. 113; Minneapolis 1948; Cambridge
1961; Cambridge, Fogg Art Museum, 1962
(summer), *Forty Master Drawings from the
Collection of John Nicholas Brown,* no. 5
Literature: Marcel Guérin, *Dix-neuf
portraits de Degas par lui-même,* Paris: M.
Guérin 1931, pl. 4; Mongan p. 66, fig. 3;
Huyghe & Jaccottet pl. 90; Rosenberg
no. 197; Alan Bowness, *Impressionists and
Post-Impressionists,* New York: Grolier,
1965, p. 215; Longstreet
PRIVATE COLLECTION

In the two years in Paris between the time
the twenty-year old Degas left Law School
to become a painter until his trip to Italy in
1856, it seems he tried to retain his own
identity by making portraits of his family
and of himself while he underwent the
conventional art education of the time in the
studio of Louis Lamothe and, in 1855, at the
Ecole des Beaux-Arts. Many of them, like
this *Self-Portrait,* were studies for paintings.
Although in the paintings the uneasy
hauteur of the artist's personality survives,
there was an effort, in the interest of
realism, to suppress the viewer's pleasure
in following the curving movements through
the wave of the hair, the brows, the nose
and the mouth. The drawing makes us
conscious, not only of this natural rhythmic
delight but also of Degas's instinctive
feeling for sculptural form which is
apparent in the variation of the weight of
the red chalk as he modeled the areas
around the eyes and the mouth.

2 MARGUERITE DE GAS C. 1854

Pencil on cream paper
11⅝ x 9½ in. (29.5 x 24 cm.)
Provenance: Fevre family; Maurice Loncle,
Paris
Literature: Jeanne Fevre, *Mon Oncle Degas,*
Geneva: Pierre Cailler, 1949, facing p. 32
STAATSGALERIE STUTTGART: GRAPHISCHE

1

Edgar Degas's younger sister, Marguerite,
was born in 1842 and in 1865 married an
architect, Henri Fevre. In 1854, at the time
of her first communion, Degas made several
drawings of her, and found her as
melancholy as he did all the members of his
family. The simplified forms of her head
are reminiscent of the Italian Renaissance
artists Degas admired, particularly Perugino
and Raphael. There is a similar suggestion
of atmosphere around the figure produced
by the pressure upon the pencil; the head is
brought out from the background by the
firm contour at the left of the head, the
heavy line behind the neck and the dark
curve through the lips. Even the allusions to
artists like Perugino and Raphael, who are
associated with religious works, strengthen
the suggestion of a touching and solemn
innocence in the portrait of twelve-year-old
Marguerite.

3 RENE DE GAS 1855-56

ATELIER stamp l.l.
Pencil on brown paper
11 7/8 x 9 1/4 in. (30.3 x 23.5 cm.)
Provenance: René de Gas;
M. Nepveu-Degas; Georges Wildenstein
Exhibitions: Paris, 1955, no. 2bis
Literature: Moskowitz & Mongan no. 775

STEPHEN R. CURRIER, NEW YORK

Although Degas in 1855 and 1856 made
many drawings of his younger brother René,
leading up to the painting which is now in
the Smith College Art Museum, this
drawing seems to be an independent work
and one which the sitter treasured and kept
in his family. The painter revealed a
touching independence in the head of this
child who was ten years old in 1855. He
placed the head of René firmly on the page.
The soft pencil lines through the hair over
the sitter's forehead carry our eyes down
through the eyebrows, along the nose and
the rest of his profile, bridging across into
his hair by the faint contours of the jaw. In
this way the drawing shows Degas's
remarkable capacity to synthesize the realism
he could absorb from Courbet or other
contemporaries with a feeling for a classically
unified, classically rhythmic composition
which he knew through the art of the past.

2

4 THERESE DE GAS c. 1855

ATELIER stamp l.l.
Pencil on buff paper
12⅝ x 11⅛ in. (32 x 28.4 cm.)
Provenance: Vente Succession de René de Gas, Hotel Drouot, Paris, November 10, 1927, no. 17
Exhibitions: Cleveland 1947, no. 54; Washington 1947, no. 25; Minneapolis 1948; New Orleans 1965, p. 57; pl. x
Literature: Philip Hendy, "Degas and the de Gas," *Bulletin of the Museum of Fine Arts,* Boston, June 1932, p. 44; Rosenberg no. 198; Longstreet

MUSEUM OF FINE ARTS, BOSTON 31.434
Julia Knight Fox Fund

Thérèse de Gas, who was to marry her cousin Edmond Morbilli (see no. 48 and nos. 21 and 22), was the elder of the painter's two sisters. She was born in Naples in 1840 and always remained closest to the Italian branch of the Degas family. In recording the complacent and impassive phase of Thérèse's adolescence (she was fifteen in 1855) Degas turned to the style of one of the artists he most admired—Ingres. Thérèse seems as self-assured and her head as firmly contoured as a woman by Ingres but her head is modeled with greater sculptural gradations and less animation. She is not as beautiful (she has not quite grown up to the Degas family nose) and her gaze seems to represent a relentless realism which one begins to suspect may have been another Degas family trait.

5 HEAD OF A ROMAN GIRL c. 1856

Pencil on gray paper
14⅞ x 10¼ in. (37.7 x 26 cm.)
Inscription: "Rome" l.r.
Provenance: René de Gas; Gustave Pellet; Maurice Exsteens; Claribel and Etta Cone
Exhibitions: Buenos Aires 1934, no. 23; New York 1945; Kansas City 1955; Baltimore 1962, no. 55
Literature: G. Jedlicka, *Galerie und Sammler,* Galerie Actuarys, Zurich, 1935, p. 473

THE BALTIMORE MUSEUM OF ART 50.12.457
Cone Collection

In going to Rome in 1856 Degas seems to have left some of his Parisian bourgeois

3

properties behind and to have drawn
sturdier figures like this Roman girl. He was
concerned with creating a suggestion of
energy by lifting the head and twisting it on
the neck and by contrasting lights and
shadows with a soft black pencil.

6 ITALIAN HEAD c. 1856

Related to VENTE IV: 94
Charcoal with estompe on yellow, wove
paper
15 x 10¼ in. (38 x 26 cm.)
Provenance: René de Gas; Gustave Pellet;
Maurice Exsteens; K. J. Thannhauser (Sale
Parke-Bernet, April 12, 1945, lot 58)
Exhibitions: Buenos Aires 1934; New York,
Weyhe, 1942, Sculptor's Drawings and
Paintings; New York 1945; Art Institute of
Chicago, 1946, *Drawings Old and New,* no.
14; New York 1947; Washington 1947, no. 3;
New York, Wildenstein, 1963; *Master
Drawings from The Art Institute of Chicago,*
no. 101
Literature: Hans Tietze, *European Master
Drawings in the United States,* New York:
J. J. Augustin, 1947, pp. 284-285, no. 142
THE ART INSTITUTE OF CHICAGO 45.37
Gift of Tiffany and Margaret Blake 1945

Degas made three other drawings of the
head of this curly-haired, bearded, and
hook-nosed Roman. In two of them the head
is lifted, the eyes raised and the mouth
opened as if the drawings were a copy of a
sixteenth- or seventeenth-century work.
The third, like this, is more quietly
introspective. In all four drawings Degas
was interested in the dramatic range
possible in a head with such forceful
features; he even made use of the open-
necked shirt to add to this impression.
The greatest theatrical power comes,
however, from the strong light and shadows
produced by the charcoal and by the use of
the estompe (or stick) to blend the charcoal
for the shadows.

7-9 *Degas seems to have spent most of the time
between October 7, 1856 and July 1, 1857,
and presumably the winter of 1857-58,
in Rome. Although there is no evidence in
the archives of the French Academy
(the Villa Medici) of Degas having worked
there, it does not seem impossible that he*

4

drew from life in its studios, perhaps with his friends Emile Lévy and Emile Delaunay. The Academy was hospitable at the time, and Degas in drawing no. 8 used the same model as his friend, Gustave Moreau, who inscribed one of his drawings of this model "Villa Medici." The one address we have for Degas in Rome, although admittedly from 1860, is the via Porta Pinciana overlooking the French Academy. In any case, whether at the Academy or not, during these years Degas made a great many studies of wirey-haired, thick-torsoed male nudes assuming traditional studio poses which were often based upon those of great works of art.

7 STANDING MALE NUDE 1856-1857

VENTE IV: 108a VENTE stamp l.r.
Pencil on greenish paper
11¾ x 8⅝ in. (30 x 22 cm.)
Inscription: "Rome 1856" l.r.
Provenance: Vente Atelier Degas IV,
July 2-4, 1919, no. 108a; Cottevielle
Literature: Reff 1964, p. 251, note 18
DAVID DANIELS, New York
Shown only at City Art Museum of
Saint Louis and Philadelphia Museum of Art.

8 STANDING MALE NUDE C. 1856-58

VENTE IV: 84c VENTE stamp l.l.
Pencil on light pink paper
11 x 7⅞ in. (28 x 20 cm.)
Provenance: Vente Atelier Degas IV,
July 2-4, 1919, no. 84c
Literature: Phoebe Pool, "Degas and
Moreau," *Burlington Magazine,* June
1963, no. 13, p. 254
CHARLES DURAND-RUEL, PARIS

9 NUDE YOUTH SEATED C. 1856-58

VENTE IV: 69a VENTE stamp l.l.
Pencil on fine-toothed cream paper
17½ x 11½ in. (44.5 x 29.2 cm.)
Inscription: "Rome" l.r.
Provenance: Vente Atelier Degas IV,
July 2-4, 1919, no. 69a; Rouart
NELSON GALLERY-ATKINS MUSEUM, KANSAS CITY
Nelson Fund

10-12 *Theodore Reff has doubted whether the dates Degas inscribed on these academic*

5

6

Rom 1856

Degas

7

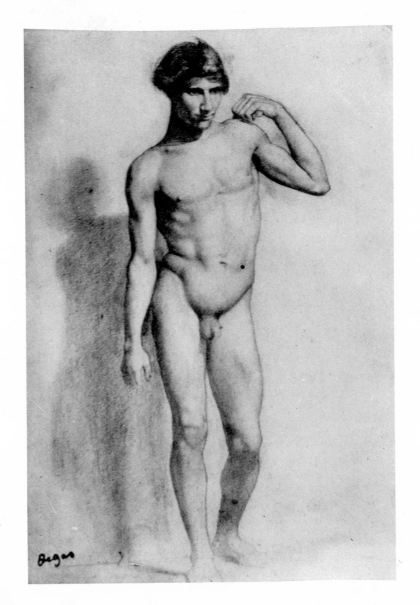

8

drawings are accurate; he suggests that some of them may have been added carelessly considerably later. He does, however, still place them between 1856 and 1858 in Rome.

In these male studios there seems to be a certain contradiction between subject matter and technique. The bodies are ungainly and the models' personalities assertive in spite of the tradition of the classically beautiful and impersonal, even anonymous, male nude; but the drawing itself is of the most meticulous pencil, applied with the greatest refinement, to sheets of decoratively coloured paper.

10 BACK OF STANDING MALE NUDE 1856-57

VENTE IV: 84d VENTE stamp l.l.
Pencil on light pink paper
11 x 7⅞ in. (28 x 20 cm.)
Inscription: "Rome 1856" l.r.
Provenance: Vente Atelier Degas IV,
July 2-4, 1919, no. 84d
Literature: Reff, 1964, p. 251, note 18
CHARLES DURAND-RUEL, PARIS

11 MALE NUDE SEATED 1857

VENTE IV: 83c VENTE stamp l.l.
Pencil on green paper
12¾ x 9¾ in. (31 x 22.5 cm.)
Provenance: Vente Atelier Degas IV,
July 2-4, 1919, no. 83c; Henriquet
Exhibitions: New York 1958, no. 5;
Minneapolis Institute of Arts, 1960, *Three Private Collections;* New York 1960, no. 70;
Baltimore 1962, no. 56; Iowa City,
University of Iowa, 1964, *Drawing and the Human Figure,* no. 93
Literature: Reff 1964, p. 251, note 19
DAVID DANIELS, NEW YORK

12 RECLINING MALE NUDE 1857

VENTE IV; 101C VENTE stamp l.l.
Pencil on pink paper
8⅛ x 11 in. (20.5 x 28 cm.)
Inscription: "Rome 1857" l.l.
Provenance: Vente Atelier Degas IV,
July 2-4, 1919, no. 101c; Viand
Literature: Reff 1964, p. 251, note 18
DAVID DANIELS, NEW YORK
Shown only at City Art Museum of
Saint Louis and Philadelphia Museum of Art

9

10

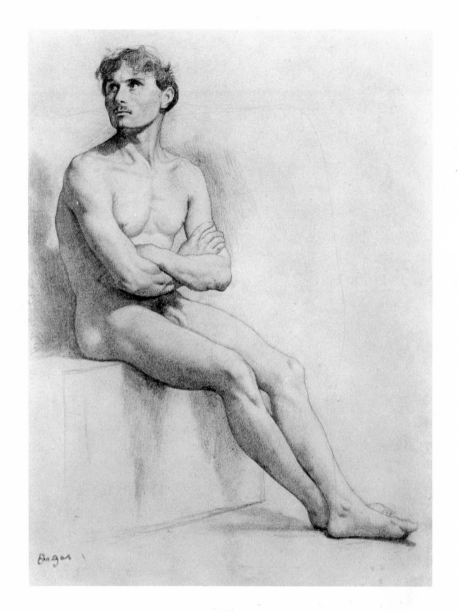

11

12

13-14 *Theodore Reff ("Copyists in the Louvre," Art Bulletin, December 1964, p. 555) has shown that there are records of Degas making formal application to copy in the Louvre for a decade—between April 7, 1855 and March 26, 1868. He also copied in the print room of the Bibliothèque Nationale and in Italy. In fact he was such an omniverous copyist from such a variety of sources that it has kept two generations of art historians busy trying to identify the originals. And the originals were sometimes the work itself and sometimes a cast, reproduction or print, sometimes sculpture and sometimes a painting, sometimes in a French museum or, on the other hand, from a fresco in an Italian church, sometimes Egyptian, sometimes Greek, sometimes by Rembrandt, sometimes Delacroix, and sometimes by Ingres. While it is difficult to establish the source, it is almost impossible to establish the date since, after all, the works were copies.*

One of Degas's sources was Marcantonio Raimondi, the sixteenth-century Florentine who made engravings after the works of artists like Raphael and Michelangelo. These were readily available in the Cabinet des Estampes at the Bibliothèque Nationale; in any case other impressions could be easily acquired. It was from two engravings after Raphael that Degas made drawing no.13; the seated draped woman and the group of figures are from Raphael's Parnassus *in the Vatican, and the two male figures under a tree from the river gods in his lost* Judgment of Paris *(the same figures which were to inspire Manet's* Déjeuner sur l'herbe*). Since the drawing is on tracing paper it is quite possible that Degas may actually have traced the original outlines with pencil and then strengthened them with pen. The twisting of the compositions on the page and the addition of another arm and a small head suggest it was a casual study.*

One of the compositions by Marcantonio which fascinated Degas was his engraving after Michelangelo's lost Battle of Cascina; *the bather on the left of drawing no. 14 is derived from it. This same figure appears three times in notebooks by Degas which are now in the Bibliothèque Nationale and can be dated from 1854 to 1857. The drawing*

13

14

here is closest in its muscularity to the last of these which suggests that late 1857 is its probable date. The second, fainter figure comes from another Marcantonio engraving —the Man with a Banner. *The appeal of both to Degas must have been in the muscular power in the Michelangelesque conception of the human body in action.*

13 *Copy of Marcantonio's engravings after Raphael's* JUDGMENT OF PARIS *and* PARNASSUS C. 1853-56.

Pen and ink on cream tracing paper
12⅛ x 6 in. (31.7 x 15.2 cm.)
Provenance: Fevre collection; anonymous gift to the Fogg Art Museum 1956
Exhibitions: Cambridge 1961, no. 12
Literature: Reff 1963, p. 238, no. 1
FOGG ART MUSEUM 1956.10
Anonymous Gift in Memory of W. G. Russell Allen

14 *Copy of* TWO NUDE MEN *after Marcantonio.* 1857

VENTE IV: 84b VENTE stamp l.l.
Pencil on pink paper
11 x 7⅞ in. (28 x 20 cm.)
Related Drawings: BN 20, p. 80; BN 17, p. 17; BN 25, p. 65; notebook formerly in the collection of Marcel Guérin p. 39
Provenance: Vente Atelier Degas IV, July 2-4, 1919, no. 84b; Durand-Ruel; John S. Newberry; his bequest to Detroit 1964
Exhibitions: Cambridge, Fogg Art Museum, 1937, *Drawings;* Exhibitions of *Collection of John S. Newberry:* Detroit Institute of Arts, 1947; Cranbrook Academy of Art Museum, 1947; Fogg Art Museum, 1948; University of Michigan Museum of Art, 1948; Buchholz Gallery, New York, 1948, no. 6; San Francisco, California Palace of the Legion of Honor, 1948; Detroit Institute of Arts, 1949, no. 10; Museum of Fine Arts, Boston, 1962, no. 33; New York, 1949, no. 6
Literature: Walker p. 184; Champigneulle p. 17; Reff 1963, p. 248; *The John S. Newberry Collection,* The Detroit Institute of Arts, Detroit, 1965, p. 33
THE DETROIT INSTITUTE OF ARTS 65.150
John S. Newberry Bequest

15

16

15-17 *Although the percentage of copies Degas made after Italian Renaissance works has been exaggerated, he did, nevertheless, copy a great many such as nos. 15-17 in the exhibition. These three drawings from Michelangelo, Botticelli and Mantegna were framed together and sold as one lot in the sale of the contents of his studio after his death. It is characteristic of Degas that two of them should have been details from paintings because even in preparing for his own work he tended to study parts rather than the composition as a whole. The three also illustrate Degas's interest in the emotionally evocative positions and gestures of the human body. The dramatic range of the three is enhanced by the pressure of his pencil—the shadows around the contours of Michelangelo's* Slave *which deepen its sensuality, the curling, wind-blown hair of Botticelli's* Venus *which in its very abundance seems to contrast with her wistful tenderness and the shading under the armpits of Mantegna's crucified thief which directs our attention to his agony.*

15 *Copy of* SLAVE *by Michelangelo in the Louvre*

VENTE IV: 99a VENTE stamp l.l.
Pencil on white paper
13 x 9 in. (33 x 23 cm.)
Related Drawings: BN carnet 10, p. 66
Provenance: Vente Atelier Degas IV,
July 2-4, 1919, no. 99a; Durand-Ruel; Peytel
collection
Literature: Walker p. 185 identified copy
MRS. MARIANNE FEILCHENFELDT, ZURICH

16 *Copy of Venus from* BIRTH OF VENUS *by Botticelli in the Uffizi*

VENTE IV: 99b VENTE stamp l.l.
Pencil on white paper
11⅜ x 8¼ in. (29 x 21 cm.)
Provenance: Vente Atelier Degas IV,
July 2-4, 1919, no. 99b; Durand-Ruel; Peytel
collection
Literature: Walker p. 185 identified copy
MRS. MARIANNE FEILCHENFELDT, ZURICH

17 *Copy of Crucified Thief from* CRUCIFIXION *by Mantegna in the Louvre*

VENTE IV: 99c VENTE stamp l.l.

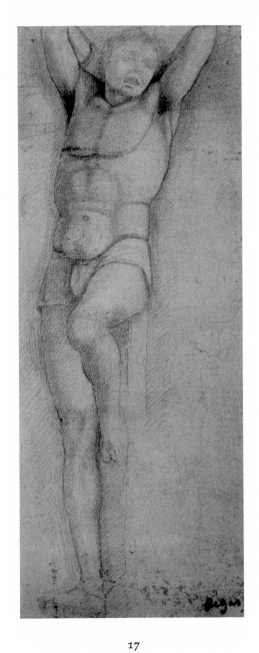

17

Pencil on white paper
12¼ x 5⅛ in. (31 x 13.5 cm.)
Provenance: Vente Atelier Degas IV,
July 2-4, 1919, no. 99c; Durand-Ruel; Peytel
collection
Literature: Reff, 1963, p. 248 identified copy
MRS. MARIANNE FEILCHENFELDT, ZURICH

18-20 *Degas's copying, which was a form of self-education in high repute in the nineteenth century, took him to drawing collections as well as to churches and museums. In the Uffizi he made a literal copy of Filippino Lippi's* Self-Portrait *(no. 18). Degas may have felt an echo of himself in Lippi's combination of uncertainty and disdain. He worked as an Italian artist might have done from the middle tone of the stained paper into the darks of the pencil and the lights of the whites.*

One artist whose subtle works Degas was often tempted to copy was Leonardo da Vinci. It was probably before he left for Italy that he drew the head of the Virgin (no. 19) from the Virgin of the Rocks *in the Louvre. Its coarse, flocked paper and the faintness of the soft pencil are characteristic of some of his earliest drawings. It shows his response to the nuances in the Leonardo—in the shadows, in the lines and in the expression. Quite different is the drawing (no. 20) from the composition of the unfinished* Adoration of the Magi *by Leonardo in Florence. In this drawing, which he dated 1860, Degas drew rapidly but as if it were a diagramatic record of the organization of the space and the movement around the dominant but gentle figures of the Virgin and Child.*

18 *Copy of* SELF-PORTRAIT *by Filippino Lippi in the Uffizi c. 1858*

Pencil, heightened with white, on brown paper
18½ x 12½ in. (47 x 31.7 cm.)
Provenance: Jeanne Fevre (niece of the painter); Gimpel fils, London
Exhibitions: London, Gimpel fils

HERMAN H. LEVY, O.B.E., HAMILTON, ONTARIO

18

19

19 *Copy of the Head of the Virgin from the*
    VIRGIN OF THE ROCKS *by Leonardo*
    in the Louvre c. 1854

    VENTE IV: 114c VENTE stamp l.l.
    Pencil, heightened with white
    11 x 6⅞ in. (28 x 17.5 cm.)
    Provenance: Vente Atelier Degas IV,
    July 2-4, 1919, no. 114c
    Exhibitions: Detroit 1941, no. 13
    Literature: Walker p. 185 identified it

    PRIVATE COLLECTION

20 *Copy of the* ADORATION OF THE MAGI *by*
    Leonardo in the Uffizi 1860

    VENTE IV: 85b VENTE stamp l.l.
    Pencil on white paper
    8¼ x 8⅝ in. (21 x 22 cm.)
    Inscription: "Florence 1860/
    Léonard de Vinci" u.r.
    Provenance: Vente Atelier Degas IV,
    July 2-4, 1919, no. 85b; Rouart
    Exhibitions: Los Angeles 1958, no. 7
    Literature: Walker p. 184 identified copy;
    Reff 1964, p. 251, note 18

    ELMER BELT LIBRARY OF VINCIANA
    University of California at Los Angeles

21-23 *In Italy Degas drew his Italian relatives as he*
       had drawn his more immediate family in
       Paris a few years before. These were
       sensitive and austere pencil drawings, often
       touched up with watercolor and pastel.
       Some were of the family of his Neapolitan-
       born father's eldest sister Rosa who was
       married to the Duke Morbilli. No. 21 is her
       son Adelchi, and no. 22 Rosa herself. These
       seem to have been independent works, but
       Degas made drawings of another aunt,
       Laura Degas Bellelli, and her family in
       preparation for his great early painting, The
       Bellelli Family, *which is now in the Louvre.*
       Baroness Bellelli's oval head, no. 23, is
       distinguished by the clarity of the modelling
       in pencil, set off by the touch of green chalk
       in the background; it does not diminish in
       quality when compared with the great
       portrait drawings of Holbein or Clouet.

21 ADELCHI MORBILLI C. 1857

    VENTE IV: 102a VENTE stamp l.l.
    Pencil & watercolor
    11⅜ x 8½ in. (29 x 21 cm.)

20

21

22

Provenance: Vente Atelier Degas IV,
July 2-4, 1919, no. 102a; Durand-Ruel
Literature: Boggs p. 125 (not illustrated);
Boggs 1963, p. 274, note 25 (not illustrated)

MR. AND MRS. NATHAN L. HALPERN, NEW YORK

22 THE DUCHESSA MORBILLI C. 1857

VENTE IV: 102b VENTE stamp l.r.
LEMOISNE 50 bis
Watercolor and pencil
13¾ x 7½ in. (35 x 19 cm.)
Provenance: Vente Atelier Degas IV,
July 2-4, 1919, no. 102b; Durand-Ruel, Paris
Exhibitions: New York, E.V. Thaw, 1964
(September 29-October 24), *19th and 20th
Century Master Drawings,* no. 10;
New Orleans 1965, p. 56, pl. IX
Literature: Boggs pp. 87, 88, note 49;
Boggs 1963; p. 272, pl. 33

MR. AND MRS. EUGENE VICTOR THAW, NEW YORK

23 BARONESS BELLELLI C. 1858

ATELIER stamp l.l.
Study for LEMOISNE 79
Pencil with green gouache on beige paper
10¼ x 8 in. (26.1 x 20.4 cm.) oval
Provenance: René de Gas (Vente Succession
de M. René de Gas, Hotel Drouot, Paris,
November 10, 1927, no. 13); acquired by the
Cabinet des Dessins of the Louvre in 1927
Exhibitions: Paris 1931, no. 90; Paris 1937,
no. 61; Rome and Milan, 1962, *Il ritratto
francese da Clouet a Degas,* no. 72, pl. XXXII
Literature: Grappe

CABINET DES DESSINS DU MUSEE DU LOUVRE
RF 11.688
Shown only at City Art Museum of
Saint Louis

24-25 *Edgar Degas was still traditional enough in
the 1850's to think of his portraits, his
academic nudes, and his copies as forms of
training for great historical works which
would draw upon his literary imagination.
In Italy he turned to the great Italian classic,
Dante's* Divine Comedy, *and for at least two
years struggled to produce a major
painting based on it. Although the studies
resulted in only two modest paintings, the
drawings in themselves reveal a great deal
about Degas. One thing is his interest in
the human body, which he depicted nude*

23

before clothing the figures with elaborate draperies. Another is his instinctive realism which meant that he drew the figure of Dante, for which the model in drawings no. 11 and 12 posed, as knottily muscled and somewhat bony.

Even more provocative than his concept of the human figure is the psychological development of the composition in relation to its source in Dante's Divine Comedy. *It seems probable that Degas was interested in the meeting of two human beings who would tentatively begin a momentous voyage together. With considerable ambivalence he could see them as Dante and Virgil or, when Virgil disappeared in the XXXth canto of the* Purgatario, *as Dante with Beatrice, who took Virgil's place. His first drawings of Beatrice, like no. 24, seem masculine, probably because Degas had been accustomed to working from the male nude in life classes in Paris and Italy. This was rectified, however, in a drawing which was clearly made from a female model for the painting and which is now in the Clark Art Institute (VENTE IV: 109d). Degas also changed his interpretation of Dante from one of abject, helpless concentration upon Beatrice (Purgatorio XXX: 79; "I shrank as a wayward child in his distress"), which is apparent in no. 24 and in the recto (not illustrated) of no. 25, to one of greater elation, the verso of no. 25, in which Dante's head is turned to contemplate Paradise ahead.*

24 *Study for* DANTE AND BEATRICE 1856-57
   VENTE IV: 116e VENTE stamp l.r.
   Study for LEMOISNE 34, 35
   Pencil on gray paper
   10 x 8¼ in. (25.4 x 21 cm.)
   Inscription: "Rome 1856" l.r.
   Related Works: VENTE IV: 116a; 109f; 116f; 109d; 108b; VENTE FEVRE: 114; DELTEIL 11
   Provenance: Vente Atelier Degas IV, July 2-4, 1919, no. 116e; Durand-Ruel; purchased by the Cincinnati Art Museum 1920
   Exhibitions: The Detroit Institute of Arts, 1950 (June-September), *Old Master Drawings from Midwestern Museums,* no. 9
   Literature: Boggs, May 1958, p. 168, note 58; Reff 1964, p. 251, note 18; Reff 1965, p. 611, note 57; Clark, vol. 1, p. 75, figure 56

   CINCINNATI ART MUSEUM

24

25

25 *Study for* DANTE AND BEATRICE 1856-57

Recto (not illustrated) and *verso* (illustrated)
VENTE IV: 105b (*recto* illustrated)
ATELIER stamp *verso* c.l.
Study for LEMOISNE 34, 35
Pencil and sanguine
12¼ x 9½ in. (31 x 24 cm.)
Inscription: "Rome 1856" *recto* l.r.
Related Works: see no. 24
Provenance: Vente Atelier Degas IV,
July 2-4, 1910, no. 105b; Durand-Ruel
Exhibitions: Los Angeles 1958, no. 11
MR. AND MRS. NORTON SIMON, LOS ANGELES

26-27 *On both sides of drawing no. 26, there are*
pencil studies of a nude Roman youth which
reveal Degas's developing interest in the
action of the human body and, in that
action, a combination of awkwardness with
potential grace which makes the youth seem
vulnerably adolescent. These are not
independent studies of a nude boy, but
studies for a composition which was never
fully realized but for which Degas made
sketches in at least five notebooks in 1857,
in addition to separate drawings like these.

The youth on the back of this drawing is
a study for an angel blowing a trumpet,
which was combined with another figure of
St. John in a watercolor (LEMOISNE 20).
Degas must have decided to reverse the
composition and, on the other side of no. 26,
he made a study for St. John which is almost
a mirror-image of an earlier preparatory
drawing (VENTE IV: 70b). *One can see the*
reversal taking place in a notebook in the
Bibliothèque Nationale in Paris (BN 25),
apparently leading to a horizontal
composition against a tropical landscape
background with a strong thrust to the right
as we see it in the body of St. John. It is to
this later stage that the watercolor of the
head of an angel (no. 27), now female,
belongs; we find the intense features of
St. John faintly drawn in the background.

The source for this subject was the
Apocalyptic vision of St. John of Ephesus,
for Degas quotes from Revelations *in the*
same Bibliothèque Nationale notebook
(BN 25, p. 39). *It does seem that he may have*
confused the two Saints John, or that one
suggested the other to him, for he dressed
the same figure in a hair-shirt in some of his

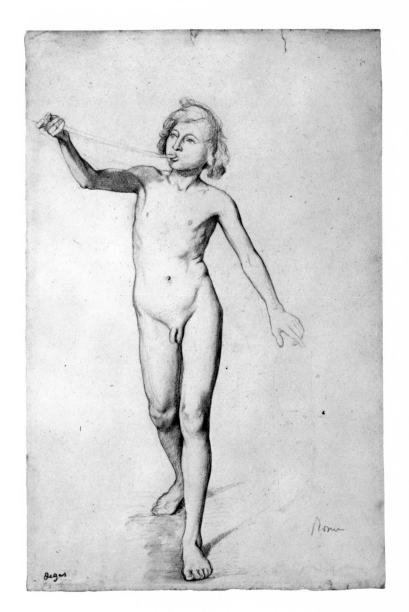

26

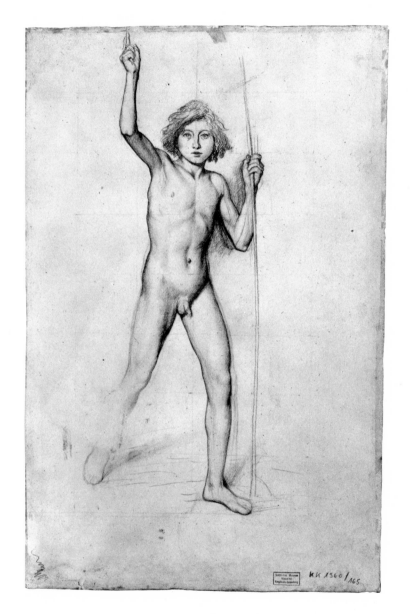

26

studies. The St. John in the exhibition was
squared for transferral, presumably to the
painting which Lemoisne (LEMOISNE 21)
may have correctly identified as St. John
the Baptist.

26 RECTO: ST. JOHN 1857

VENTE IV: 70b
Study for LEMOISNE 21
Pencil and watercolor

Verso: The Angel
VENTE stamp l.l.
Study for LEMOISNE 20
Pencil
Inscription: "Rome" l.r.
17½ x 11⁷⁄₁₆ in. (44.5 x 29 cm.)
Related Material: BN 13, p. 48; BN 28, pp.
34-36, 49; BN 17, pp. 9, 11, 15, 29, 42, 43, 55;
BN 25, pp. 26, 33, 35, 39, 40, 49, 51
Provenance: Vente Atelier Degas IV, July
2-4, 1919, no. 70b; Bernheim-Jeune; Tanner;
Collection Dr. Eduard Freiherr von der
Heydt, Ascona; his gift to the Von der Heydt
Museum, 1952
Literature: Von der Heydt Museum,
Wuppertal, *Verzeichnis der Handzeich-*
nungen Pastelle und Aquarelle, 1965, no. 38

VON DER HEYDT MUSEUM, WUPPERTAL

27 *Angel Blowing a Trumpet for* ST. JOHN AND
THE ANGEL 1857

VENTE IV: 100c VENTE stamp l.l.
Pencil and watercolor on paper with
Mill watermark l.r.
12 x 16 in. (35 x 40.6 cm.)
Inscription: "Rome" l.r.
Provenance: Vente Atelier Degas IV,
July 2-4, 1919, no. 100c; Durand-Ruel
Exhibitions: Fort Worth Art Center, 1965,
Master Drawings from Degas to
Lichtenstein, cover
Literature: Sixty-ninth Annual Report,
Museum of Art, Carnegie Institute,
Pittsburgh, 1965, cover

MUSEUM OF ART, CARNEGIE INSTITUTE,
PITTSBURGH

28-29 *From 1859 to 1860 Degas made studies for*
the largest canvas he was ever to paint, the
Daughter of Jephthah. *In it there were*
reminiscences, as both Mr. Fries and
Mr. Reff have pointed out, of the two quite

27

different artists whose works, among others, he was copying at this time—Mantegna and Delacroix.

The subject was taken from Judges, the story of the Gileadite, Jephthah, who in return for victory against the Ammonites, promises the Lord that we will offer the first person who leaves his house to greet him on his return as "a burnt offering" to the Lord. The narrative continues, "and, behold, his daughter came out to meet him with timbrels and with dances: and she was his only child; beside her he had neither son nor daughter. And it came to pass, when he saw her, that he rent his clothes." In the compositional drawing (no. 28) Jephthah on horseback and all his companions turn away from the spectacle of the women greeting them on the hill; in the final painting there is a more dramatic confrontation between the men and the women.

The other drawing (no. 29) is characteristically a study of two of the women nude—their bodies worked out in this fashion before Degas clothed them in the final painting. The one on the right is presumably the daughter of Jephthah, her gesture suggestive of both welcome and withdrawal. She already seems to anticipate the time to come "in which she went with her companions, and bewailed her virginity upon the mountains."

28 *Compositional Study for* THE DAUGHTER OF JEPHTHAH 1859-60

VENTE IV: 118a VENTE stamp l.r.
Atelier stamp l.l.
Study for LEMOISNE 94
Pencil
7¼ x 10¼ in. (sight) (19 x 26 cm.)
Provenance: Vente Atelier Degas IV,
July 2-4, 1919, no. 118a; Jamot; private
collection, Paris; Michel N. Benisovich,
New York
Exhibitions: New York 1949, no. 10; Toledo
1950; London, Wildenstein, 1953
(May 14-July 4), *The Art of Drawing
1500-1950,* no. 89; New York 1960, no. 76
Literature: Jere Abbott, "La Fille de Jephté,"
Smith College Bulletin, June 1934, p. 4,
figure 1; Eleanor Mitchell, "La Fille de Jephté
par Degas," *Gazette des Beaux-Arts,* 1937,

28

p. 181, figure 10; Rewald 1961, p. 58
Related Material: Boggs, June 1958,
pp. 200-202 nos. BII, III, IV, V, VI, VII; Reff
1963, p. 242; Reff 1964, p. 252; G. Friez,
"Degas et les Maîtres," *Art de France*, 1964,
p. 335; Reff, December 1965, pp. 612-613
nos. 12, 26, 27, 1, 19.

WILDENSTEIN AND COMPANY, INC., NEW YORK

29 *Study for* THE DAUGHTER OF JEPHTHAH
1859-60

VENTE IV: 125a   VENTE stamp l.l.
Study for LEMOISNE 94
Pencil on smooth cream paper, folded
in center
10⅜ x 15⅜ in. (26.4 x 38.9 cm.)
Provenance: Vente Atelier Degas IV,
July 2-4, 1919, no. 125a; Dr. Georges Viau;
Dr. Grete Ring; her bequest 1954
Literature: University of Oxford, *Report
of the Visitors of the Ashmolean Museum,*
1954, p. 48

VISITORS OF THE ASHMOLEAN MUSEUM, OXFORD
Bequest of Dr. Grete Ring

30-32 *These three drawings were all listed in the
fourth sale of the contents of Degas's studio
after his death as studies for* The Daughter
of Jephthah. *They cannot, however, be
directly related to any figure in the final
painting, and only no. 31 which could be the
figure who flings himself against Jephthah's
horse, suggests any connection with the
pencil compositional study (no. 28).*

*They show Degas's increasingly powerful
handling of the human body in movement.
In drawing no. 32 the pressures and
accenting in the draughtsmanship, as much
as the anatomical description, give the figure
the suggestion of speed. A quality of haste
even emerges from the movement, the
hesitancy and the repetitions in the penciled
lines.*

*There is also a sense of pathos in the figures.
The crouching shoulders and shadowed face
of no. 31 suggest his anguish. And the boy
in no. 30 throws his body forward in a
gesture of youthful despair. It is as if Degas
were studying the ways in which the human
body could express the shock of the men at
Mizpeh witnessing the sacrifice of the
daughter of Jephthah.*

29

30 *Study for* THE DAUGHTER OF JEPHTHAH
1859-60

VENTE IV: 118c VENTE stamp l.l.
Atelier stamp l.l.
Study for LEMOISNE 94
Pencil
14⅛ x 9¼ (36 x 23.5 cm.)
Provenance: Vente Atelier Degas IV,
July 2-4, 1919, no. 118c; Paul Jamot,
Alan Burroughs, Little Compton, R.I.;
Michel N. Benisovich
Literature: Jere Abbott, "La Fille de Jepthé,"
Smith College Bulletin,
June 1934, p. 3, note 1 (not illustrated)
GREGOIRE TARNOPOL, NEW YORK

31 *Study for* THE DAUGHTER OF JEPHTHAH

VENTE IV: 119b VENTE stamp l.l.
ATELIER stamp l.r.
Study for LEMOISNE 94
Pencil on light beige paper
12¼ x 8½ (31 x 21.5 cm.)
Provenance: Vente Atelier Degas IV, July
2-4, 1919, no. 119b
CHARLES DURAND-RUEL, PARIS

32 *Study for* THE DAUGHTER OF JEPHTHAH
1859-60

VENTE IV: 119c VENTE and ATELIER stamps l.r.
Study for LEMOISNE 94
Pencil on light beige paper
12¼ x 8½ (31 x 21.5 cm.)
Provenance: Vente Atelier Degas IV,
July 2-4, 1919, no. 119c
CHARLES DURAND-RUEL, PARIS

33 *Compositional Study for* THE YOUNG
SPARTANS 1860

VENTE stamp l.l.
Study for LEMOISNE 71
Pencil
7¾ x 11½ in. (sight) (19.7 x 29.2 cm.)
Related Studies: BN 16 p. 87; BN I pp. 36,
147
Provenance: Atelier Degas; probably *Vente
Atelier Degas* I, May 6-8, 1918, no. 62b;
otherwise VENTE V; private collection,
England
Exhibitions: New York 1960, no. 73
Literature: Douglas Cooper, "List of
Emendations to the Courtauld's Catalogue,"

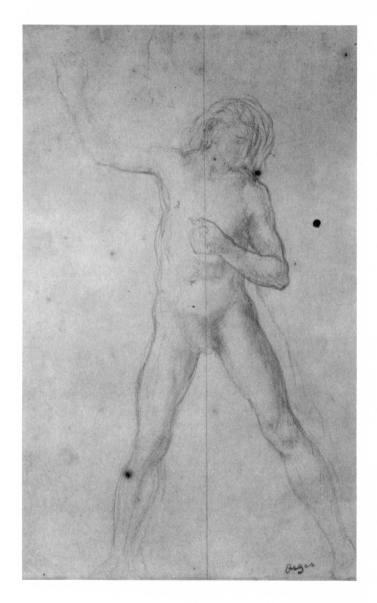

30

Degas

31

Burlington, April 1954, p. 120.
WILDENSTEIN AND COMPANY, INC., NEW YORK

Of all Degas's paintings of historical subjects the most completely resolved is the final version of *The Young Spartans* which is in the National Gallery of London. The compositional study in this exhibition is actually closer to another earlier version in the Art Institute of Chicago in which Degas made some adjustments in the arrangement, most conspicuously by removing the pitched roof from the building in the background. In that building and in the dressing of the hair there was an effort to give *The Young Spartans* a suggestion of remoteness in time and space which was abandoned in the final version. The essentials of the subject are nevertheless there—the young Spartan girls who, under the gaze of their elders including Lycurgus, challenge a group of youths to a wresting game. Degas's source was Plutarch, perhaps with the addition, as Douglas Cooper has pointed out, of the Abbé Barthélemy's *Voyage du jeune Anarchis.*

34 *Nude Youth for* THE YOUNG SPARTANS 1860

VENTE stamp l.l.
Study for LEMOISNE 70
Pencil on white paper
11¼ x 7 in. (sight) (28.5 x 17.7 cm.)
Provenance: Atelier Degas; probably *Vente Atelier Degas* I, May 6-8, 1918, no. 62b; otherwise VENTE V; Marius de Zayas (Sale, Anderson, New York, March 23, 1923, no. 70)?; Dan Fellows Platt (Sale 1949, no. 69); Victor Spark 1949; John S. Newberry; his bequest to Detroit 1964
Exhibitions: Detroit Institute of Arts, 1932, *Drawings from Collection of Dan Fellows Platt,* no. 107 or 108; Detroit Institute of Arts, 1951 (May 15-Oct. 7), *25 Recent Additions to the Collection of John S. Newberry,* no. 13; Cambridge, Fogg Art Museum, 1958, *Watercolors etc. from Collections of Members of Class of 1933,* no. 18; Cambridge, Fogg Art Museum, 1960, *Thirty-three French Drawings from the Collection of John S. Newberry,* no. 6; Detroit Institute of Arts, 1962, *French Drawings and Water Colors from Michigan Collections,* no. 49
Literature: Moskowitz & Mongan no. 777; *The John S. Newberry Collection,* The Detroit Institute of Arts, Detroit, 1965, p. 33

32

33

THE DETROIT INSTITUTE OF ARTS 65.149
John S. Newberry Bequest

By comparing this study for the youth at the left of the group of boys in *The Young Spartans*, with the drawings for *St. John and the Angel* (no. 26) which are some three years earlier, we can see how much more fluid and open Degas's drawing had become, the very softness of the contours fusing the body into the space around it. Nonetheless, if we compare it with a drawing for the *Daughter of Jephthah* (no. 30), we find that he was actually making his line crisper and modeling with greater clarity than he had the year before. In his concentration upon the torso and upper arms in this drawing and in the upward motion which surges through the figure we feel Degas's increased self-assurance in depicting the human body with his pencil.

35 *Study for* THE YOUNG SPARTANS EXERCISING 1860

VENTE stamp l.l.
Study for LEMOISNE 70
Pencil on irregularly-cut, fairly fine manila paper
9 x 14 in. (22.8 x 35.6 cm.)
Provenance: Atelier Degas; probably *Vente Atelier Degas* I, May 6-8, 1918, no. 62b; otherwise VENTE V; Marius de Zayas (Sale, Anderson Galleries, New York, March 23-24, 1923)
Exhibitions: Ann Arbor, University of Michigan, 1962, *A Generation of Draughtsmen*
Literature: Douglas Cooper, "List of Emendations to the Courtauld's Catalogue," *Burlington*, April 1954, p. 120

THE TOLEDO MUSEUM OF ART 23.62
Museum Purchase 1923

Although Degas always loved the classical tradition in literature, history or art, which he had absorbed as a student at his lycée, he nevertheless saw it in terms of the world he knew. As Lemoisne points out (LEMOISNE I, p. 42) Degas's young Spartans suggest Montmartre rather than ancient Greece. The crawling youth in no. 35 is far removed from the boy who had posed for Degas in Rome in 1856 (no. 9); and the difference is not in his being Parisian rather than Roman. Degas was now choosing poses

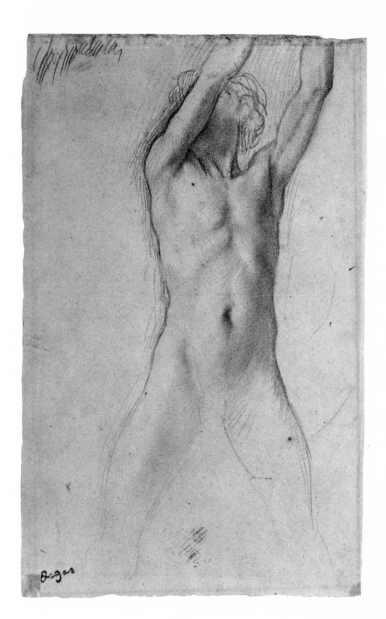

34

35

which involved more physical strain and a ready agility rather than weariness. The tension and the animation is emphasized by the spirited accenting of some of the lines (instead of the consistent, gradual modeling in the earlier drawing). There has also been an important psychological change in the way this youth meets an external challenge; whereas the other was unhappily withdrawn.

36 *Crawling Nude Youth for*
THE YOUNG SPARTANS 1860

VENTE stamp l.l.
Study for LEMOISNE 70
Oil on dark oiled paper
9½ x 12½ in (24.2 x 31.7 cm.)
Provenance: Atelier Degas; probably *Vente Atelier Degas* I, May 6-8, 1918, no. 62b; otherwise VENTE V; gift of Mrs. Mary Woodard Reinhardt 1927
Exhibitions: Cambridge 1929, no. 26; Northampton 1933, no. 23; Cleveland 1947, no. 56; Cambridge 1961, no. 15
Literature: Mongan & Sachs no. 661; Douglas Cooper, "List of Emendations to the Courtauld's Catalogue," *Burlington*, April 1954, p. 120
FOGG ART MUSEUM 1927.62
Courtesy of Mrs. Woodard Reinhardt

The pencil drawing of the crawling youth in no. 35 was squared for transferral to another surface—presumably to the oiled paper upon which Degas developed this same figure thinking in terms of light and shadow as he modeled the darks and the lights with thin oil paint. He also strengthened the figure, spreading the arms apart in a more simian fashion, making the head bolder, preoccupied and challenging.

37 *Study for* SEMIRAMIS 1860-61

VENTE IV: 125b VENTE stamp l.l.
Study for LEMOISNE 82
Pencil on smooth white paper
11½ x 8¾ (29.2 x 21.2 cm.)
Provenance: Vente Atelier Degas IV, July 2-4, 1919, no. 125b; Dr. Georges Viau; Dr. Grete Ring; her bequest 1954
Literature: University of Oxford, *Report of the Visitors of the Ashmolean Museum* 1954, p. 48 (not illustrated)
VISITORS OF THE ASHMOLEAN MUSEUM, OXFORD
Bequest of Dr. Grete Ring

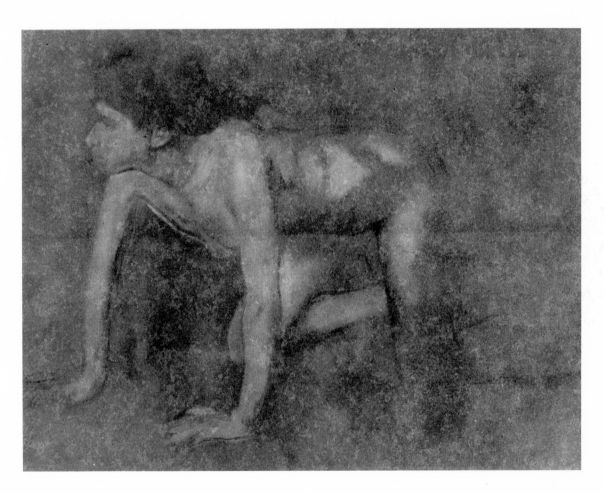

36

Degas's notebooks and copies of the early 1860s show him to have been enchanted with the idea of Egypt and the Near East, and throughout his life he remained delighted by the Arabian legends of the *Thousand and One Nights*. It was natural that he should have decided to recreate one of the most colorful moments in Near Eastern legendary history, that of the beautiful Oriental Queen Semiramis looking down at the city of Babylon which she had built on the Euphrates. As Miss Browse has shown (Browse p. 50) Degas's interest in the subject was stimulated also by his love of Opera; and the painting may actually have been based upon a production of *Semiramis* which had been staged at the *Opéra* in 1860. The finished work, now in the Louvre, has the sweep and the shallowness of an operatic stage, and the figures in this setting have a ceremonial dignity. This is reflected in the ritualistic quality of the study of two ladies-in-waiting to the Queen (no. 37), their hands weighted down so convincingly with the symbols of her authority.

38 *Study for* SEMIRAMIS 1860-61
VENTE I: 7b VENTE stamp l.r.

Study for LEMOISNE 82
Black pencil and estompe, touched with green crayon on cream paper
10½ x 13¾ in. (26.7 x 34.8 cm.)
Provenance: Vente Atelier Degas I, May 6-8, 1918, no. 7b; acquired by the Luxembourg Museum, Paris; transferred to the Louvre 1930
Literature: Lafond vol. I, between pp. 36 and 37
CABINET DES DESSINS DU MUSEE DU LOUVRE
RF 15530
Shown only at City Art Museum of Saint Louis

An imposing part of the procession behind Semiramis is the chariot-horse which stands with the pride and self-control of an operatic animal. He seems a descendant of Greek horses, even of those in the Panathenaic procession of the Parthenon frieze, which Degas had been copying since 1854. It is significant that the horse plays such an important role in this work since Degas was beginning to study horses more frequently in his drawings and paintings.

37

38

39-41 *These three drawings are studies for the first work Degas exhibited at the Salon: the* Scène de Guerre au Moyen Age, *which by 1918 had become the even more romantic and ambiguous* Malheurs de la Ville d'Orléans. *The investigations of Cabanne (*Gazette des Beaux-Arts, *May 1962, pp 363-6) and Miss Pool (*Apollo, *October 1964, pp. 306-311) have failed to find a historic or literary source for the work. One wonders whether there may not be some ironic commentary on contemporary events in New Orleans where the painter's mother had been born.*

The Crouching Nude *(no. 7) is a study for a preliminary composition in the Cabinet des Dessins at the Louvre. It shows with what little inhibition Degas was now drawing the female nude body. The pencil has been pressed down heavily in certain areas so that there is a sense of light, and even color, in addition to the definition of form. The nude herself, with her small breasts, and her stomach and shoulders sagging, seems stunned into a state of shock by the ravage that is taking place.*

The other two drawings are studies of an archer, a girl in boy's dress, who in the final work rides beside a more militaristically armoured figure. The pencil drawing of her nude shows her worried concern, which becomes more apparent in the deep frown of the dressed figure. A comparison of the two reveals how delicately and descriptively Degas worked with pencil, as in the girl's short hair, and yet how much more curtly and suggestively when he used the broader and softer conte crayon.

39 *Nude for the* MALHEURS DE LA VILLE D'ORLEANS
   1865

VENTE I: 13 VENTE stamp l.l.
ATELIER stamp *verso*
Study for LEMOISNE 124
Black pencil on beige paper
12¼ x 10⅞ in. (31.1 x 27.6 cm.)
Provenance: Vente Atelier Degas I, May 6-8, 1918, no. 13; acquired by the Luxembourg Museum; transferred to the Louvre 1930
Exhibitions: Rome, Palazzo di Venezia, 1959-60 (December 18-February 14), *Il disegno francese,* no. 180; Paris, Cabinet des Dessins du Musée du Louvre, 1964, *Dessins de*

39

sculpteurs de Pajou à Rodin, no. 68
CABINET DES DESSINS DU MUSEE DU LOUVRE
RF 12.265
Shown only at City Art Museum of
Saint Louis

40 *Archer for the* MALHEURS DE LA VILLE
D'ORLEANS 1865

VENTE I: 13 VENTE stamp l.l.
ATELIER stamp *verso*
Study for LEMOISNE 124
Black pencil on fine gray paper
9 x 14 in. (22.8 x 35.6 cm.)
Provenance: Vente Atelier Degas I, May 6-8,
1918, no. 13; acquired by the Luxembourg
Museum; transferred to the Louvre 1930
Exhibitions: Paris 1924, no. 85a; Brussels
1936, *Dessins français*, no. 98; Strasbourg
1947, *De Manet à Bonnard*
CABINET DES DESSINS DU MUSEE DU LOUVRE
RF 15.522
Shown only at City Art Museum of
Saint Louis

41 *Archer for the* MALHEURS DE LA VILLE
D'ORLEANS 1865

VENTE I: 13 VENTE stamp l.l.
ATELIER stamp *verso*
Study for LEMOISNE 124
Black pencil, sanguine and white crayon on
fine gray paper
9 x 14 in. (22.9 x 35.5 cm.)
Provenance: Vente Atelier Degas I, May 6-8,
1918, no. 13; acquired by the Luxembourg
Museum; transferred to the Louvre 1930
Literature: Rivière no. 14; Pecírka no. 6
CABINET DES DESSINS DU MUSEE DU LOUVRE
RF 15.535
Shown only at City Art Museum of
Saint Louis

42 HORSE 1860-65

VENTE IV: 201b VENTE stamp l.l.
ATELIER stamp *verso*
Pencil on light brown paper
12⅝ x 9⅞ in. (32.2 x 25.8 cm.)
Provenance: Vente Atelier Degas IV, July
2-4, 1919, no. 201b; Dr. Gustav Radeke;
gift of Mrs. Gustav Radeke to RISD
Museum 1921
Exhibitions: Cleveland 1947, no. 61;

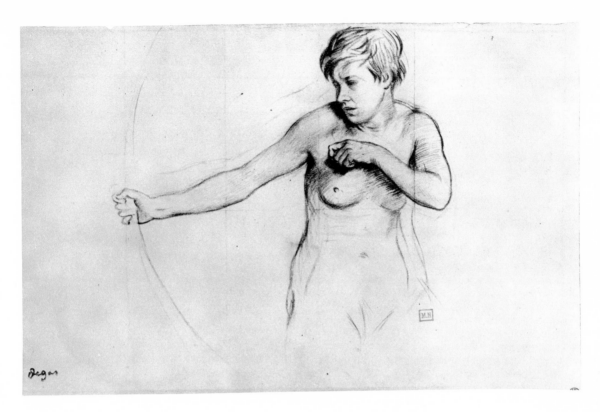

40

41

Washington 1947, no. 22
Literature: James Fowle, "A Note on Degas,"
*Bulletin of the Rhode Island School of
Design,* December 1964, p. 19, figure 11
MUSEUM OF ART, RHODE ISLAND SCHOOL OF
DESIGN, PROVIDENCE 21.127
Gift of Mrs. Gustav Radeke

Although horses played important roles in
three of Degas's historical canvases,
Daughter of Jephthah (1859-60), *Semiramis*
(1860-61) and *Scène de Guerre au Moyen
Age* (1865), they were derived from works of
art—from the Parthenon, from Delacroix
and, as Miss Pool points out (*Apollo,*
October 1964, p. 311), from the
Belgian 19th century painter, Joseph Liés.
Even his earliest race-track paintings
(LEMOISNE 75, 76, 101), which were at least
begun by 1862, were influenced a great deal
by Delacroix, Géricault and English animal
painters. Nevertheless he was at this same
period extending his interest in horses to
studies from life—probably at the Norman
estate of a school-friend, Paul Valpinçon,
which was close to one of the great
horse-breeding establishments in France,
Haras-le-pin. This quiet and, in some ways,
still tentative drawing could have been made
in Normandy. We seem to feel Degas's eyes
and hand at work before a moving animal
from the repetition of the lines and the
tenderly unflattering record of actuality in
its angularity and scrawny head. (see no. 59)

43 AMAZON C. 1866

VENTE IV: 237d   VENTE stamp l.l.
Pencil on white paper
13 x 9 in. (33 x 23 cm.)
Related Works: VENTE IV: 221b; 235a; 237a;
238
Provenance: Vente Atelier Degas IV, July
2-4, 1919, no. 237d
Exhibitions: The Montreal Museum of Fine
Arts, 1953, *Five Centuries of Drawings,*
no. 206
Literature: Bouret p. 48

BARONESS ALAIN DE GUNZBURG, PARIS

At Paul Valpinçon's Norman estate,
Ménil-Hubert, Degas studied the way riders
sat on their horses as well as the horses
themselves. One series depicted a
full-skirted female rider or, as the French
call her, an Amazon. From these drawings

43

42

grew a painting of a family outing on horseback (LEMOISNE 117), perhaps his Valpinçon friends. This particular pose is repeated in drawings of a swiftly moving horse as if horse and rider were participating in a steeplechase or hunt. Degas placed his figures in space so that we seem to be on the ground looking up at the compactly drawn rider who is so convincingly balanced on her horse.

44 *Study for the* SCENE DE STEEPLE-CHASE 1866

VENTE IV: 232b VENTE stamp l.l.
Study for LEMOISNE 140
Pencil and charcoal
13¾ x 8⅞ in. (35 x 22.5 cm.)
Related Studies: LEMOISNE 141, 142; VENTE IV: 227b, 245d, 241a, 273a; VENTE III: 141(2), 91(2); LEMOISNE 144; VENTE IV: 241b; LEMOISNE 143; VENTE IV: 234b, 234c, 216a; VENTE II: 236(2); VENTE IV: 225b
Provenance: Vente Atelier Degas IV, July 2-4, 1919, no. 232b; Vignier; bought from Durand-Ruel 1950
Exhibitions: Bern 1951-52, no. 87

BARON LOUIS DE CHOLLET, FRIBOURG

In 1866 Degas exhibited at the Salon his *Scène de Steeple-Chase: Aux courses, le jockey blessé,* a large painting with a theatrical subject, the jockey thrown from his horse and wounded, if not dying, during the cross-country obstacle race known as the Steeplechase. The subject itself was timely because steeplechasing had just been re-established in France with the foundation of the *Société des Steeplechases de France* in 1863. This drawing must have been one of the first studies for the large painting. At the bottom Degas lightly drew the movement of the racers toward the right with a single horse bolting away toward the left; above this, three riderless horses move in different directions with a horse and rider approaching and the thrown figure of a jockey lying prone on the ground. The horses in the drawing are more spontaneous than those in the final painting.

45 *Wounded Jockey for the*
SCENE DE STEEPLE-CHASE 1866

VENTE III: 353 (2) VENTE stamp l.r.
Study for LEMOISNE 140

44

45

Charcoal

9 x 12¼ in. (23 x 31 cm.)

Provenance: Vente Atelier Degas III, April
7-9, 1919, no. 353 (2); bought from R. Balay,
New York 1950

BARON LOUIS DE CHOLLET, FRIBOURG

The principal figure in the final version of
the *Steeple-Chase* is the wounded jockey
who lies helplessly and prosaically on the
ground. He may be dying, but Degas painted
him with the same supreme indifference to
this dramatic possibility that Manet had
revealed two years earlier in his *Dying
Toreador*, now in the National Gallery in
Washington. Degas, perhaps as a result of
conversations with Manet whom he had met
early in the 1860's, was now making his
works as factual and as pedestrian as
possible, the antithesis of the eloquence the
official Salon preferred. As a result the
charcoal drawing of the wounded jockey is
suggested with lines that are abrupt, and
curt and in themselves a contradiction of
academic niceties, if forceful reminders of
life's realities.

46 FOUR STUDIES OF A JOCKEY C. 1866

VENTE III: 114 (1) VENTE stamp l.l.

LEMOISNE 158

Sepia and gouache on brown wove paper
with *Canson frères* watermark

17¾ x 12⅜ in. (45 x 31.5 cm.)

Provenance: Vente Atelier Degas III, April
7-9, 1919, no. 114 (1); Nunès, Paris; gift of
Mrs. L. L. Coburn, 1933

Exhibitions: Oakland and Seattle 1939;
Art Institute of Chicago 1946, *Drawings
Old and New*, no. 15; Cleveland 1947,
no. 63; Los Angeles 1958, no. 16; New York,
Wildenstein, 1963, *Master Drawings from
the Art Institute of Chicago*, no. 103

Literature: Vingt Dessins, no. 7; P. A.
Lemoisne, *Degas*, Paris: Librairie Centrale
des Beaux-Arts, 1911, p. 35, pl. x; Lemoisne
no. 158; Shoolman & Slatkin pl. 100;
Huyghe pl. 37; Moskowitz & Mongan no.
778; M. Sérullaz, *Drawings of the French
Impressionists*, New York: Shorewood,
1962, p. 71; P. Elgar, *Degas Courses*, Paris:
Hazan, 1965, pl. 15

THE ART INSTITUTE OF CHICAGO 33.469
Gift of Mr. and Mrs. L. L. Coburn

46

In Degas's lifetime the gouache drawings of jockeys, which Lemoisne numbers 151-162, were dated 1866, a date which we have no reason to doubt. The browned paper of the Chicago drawing has the quality of parchment as a foil for the brilliant contrasts of the lights and darks of the gouache and the sepia ink, both laid on with a brush. The sparkle of the jockey's silks is increased by the brilliance of their blues and whites against the warm browns. The repetition of the body of the single jockey and the strength of its placement back into space reminds us of Watteau.

47 MME JULIE BURTIN 1863-1866

VENTE II: 347 VENTE stamp l.l.
Study for LEMOISNE 108
Graphite pencil with touches of white chalk on white paper (watermark: tree with circle)
14¼ x 10¾ in. (36.2 x 27.3 cm.)
Inscription: "Mme Julie Burtin" u.r.
Provenance: Vente Atelier Degas II, December 11-13, 1918, no. 347 Reginald Davis; Mme Demotte in 1924; acquired by Paul J. Sachs July 1928; bequest of Meta and Paul J. Sachs 1965
Exhibitions: Paris 1924, no. 81; Cambridge 1929, no. 32; New York 1930, no. 17; Boston 1935, no. 119; Buffalo 1935, no. 114; Philadelphia 1936, no. 64; Paris 1937, no. 69; Brooklyn 1939; Washington, Phillips Gallery, 1940, *Modern Drawings*; Detroit 1941, no. 16; New York 1945, no. 57; Wellesley 1946; San Francisco 1947, no. 87; New York 1947; Minneapolis 1948; Detroit Institute of Arts, 1951, *French Drawings from the Fogg Museum of Art*, no. 33; Richmond 1952; Waterville, Maine, Colby College, 1956, *Drawings*; Los Angeles 1958, no. 13; Rotterdam & Paris 1958-59, no. 160; New York 1959, no. 160; Cambridge 1965 and New York 1967, no. 55
Literature: Rivière no. 26; Mongan pp. 64-66 and cover; Schwabe p. 8; Mongan & Sachs no. 663; James Watrous, *The Craft of Old-Master Drawings*, Madison: the University of Wisconsin Press, 1957, pp. 141 (ill.), 144-145; Rosenberg no. 201; Boggs no. 35; Clark vol. I, p. 80, figure 62; Reff, December 1965, p. 613, note 88; Longstreet

47

FOGG ART MUSEUM 1965.254
Bequest of Meta and Paul J. Sachs 1965

Shown only at Philadelphia Museum of Art
and the Minneapolis Institute of Arts

In this drawing there is the most exquisite
harmony between the refinement and
understatement of the drawing and the
personality of the sitter. The hand had
become an expressive instrument for Degas,
no longer the gauche embarrassment of the
1850's; and much of the character of Mme
Burtin is conveyed by her fingers plucking at
her delicate shawl. Although we know
nothing about this sitter there is no reason to
assume (see Reff, December 1965, p. 613,
note 88) that the name should be read
"Barley." In the drawing in the Clark Art
Institute, Williamstown, which is dated
1863, there is quite clearly inscribed another
variant of her name, "Mme Jules Bertin."
A later notebook in the Bibliothèque
Nationale (BN 8, pp. 37, 41) has drawings
which suggest that although Degas may
have drawn the head of Mme Burtin in 1863,
he worked upon the three-quarters seated
portrait of her, as we find her in this
drawing, about 1866.

48 EDMONDO MORBILLI c. 1865

ATELIER stamp (faded sepia) *verso*
Study for LEMOISNE 164
Charcoal on white paper
12⅛ x 9 in. (31.7 x 22.8 cm.)
Inscription: "Marie Louise" *verso*
Provenance: Vente René de Gas, Hotel
Drouot, Paris, November 10, 1927, no. 9;
purchased from Wildenstein May 28, 1931
Exhibitions: Cambridge 1934, no. 152;
Philadelphia 1936, no. 72; Paris 1937, no.
76; Cleveland 1947, no. 65; Washington
1947, no. 21; Minneapolis 1948; Montreal
Museum of Fine Arts, 1953 (October-
November), *Five Centuries of Drawings,*
no. 208; Rotterdam & Paris 1958, no. 162;
New York 1959, no. 162
Literature: Philip Hendy, "Degas and the
de Gas," *Bulletin of the Museum of Fine
Arts,* Boston, June 1932, p. 44; Mongan p.
64, figure 2; Shoolman & Slatkin pl. 104;
Longstreet

MUSEUM OF FINE ARTS, BOSTON 31.433
Julia Knight Fox Fund

This drawing of the head of Edmondo

48

Morbilli is clearly a study for the double portrait with his wife, the painter's sister Thérèse (see no. 4); the painting, which like the drawing, is in the Museum of Fine Arts in Boston, must have been done after their marriage in 1863. Edmondo, who was a first cousin of Edgar Degas, was the son of Rose Degas Morbilli (see no. 22) and the brother of Adelchi (see no. 21). Although in the drawing Degas applied soft strokes of charcoal quite crisply to give the relief-like modeling to the head, its effect is soft, and the head of Edmondo Morbilli seems mobile but idealized. In the painting he was to become more awesomely arrogant.

49-50 *By 1866 Degas was inclined to think of people, even when he painted their portraits, as part of their normal environment. When he decided to paint the young artist, Victoria Dubourg, he placed her in the kind of drawing room in which those characteristically Parisian nineteenth-century receptions, at which young artists and writers would gather, were held. Degas and Mlle Dubourg were part of a circle which included the Manets, the Morisots and the handsome painter, Fantin-Latour, whom she would marry in 1876.*

Degas did indicate something of the setting in this developed drawing (no. 49), even by placing Mlle Dubourg somewhat to the right of the centre of the picture and thus indicating that this is not the symmetrical space of pictorial convention but the casual glimpse of space we experience in life. It is Mlle Dubourg, herself, who creates the environment most effectively by leaning over to us with the interested preoccupation in someone else she must have habitually revealed.

Her hands, which Degas studied separately, are solid, firmly clasped, but held forward beyond her knees as a gesture of her projection beyond herself. The degree to which Degas used a gesture interpretatively can be seen by comparing this with the drawing of Mme Burtin (no. 47). Even Degas's pencil seems firmer and more decisive in indicating Mlle Dubourg's more forthright personality.

49

49 MLLE VICTORIA DUBOURG 1866

VENTE II: 239 (3) VENTE stamp l.l.
Study for LEMOISNE 137
Pencil
14 x 11¾ in. (35.5 x 30 cm.)
Provenance: Vente Atelier Degas II,
December 11-13, 1918, no. 239 (3);
M. Lazare Weiller
Exhibitions: Paris 1924, no. 96; Paris 1931,
no. 116; Baltimore 1962, no. 58
PAUL-LOUIS WEILLER, PARIS

50 HANDS OF MLLE DUBOURG 1866

VENTE II: 239 (2) VENTE stamp l.l.
Study for LEMOISNE 137
Pencil on white paper
6⅝ x 8¾ in. (17 x 22.3 cm.)
Provenance: Vente Atelier Degas II,
December 11-13, 1918, no. 239 (2);
M. Lazare Weiller
Exhibitions: Paris 1924, no. 97; Paris 1931,
no. 116; Baltimore 1962, no. 59
Literature: Boggs no. 51, p. 31
PAUL-LOUIS WEILLER, PARIS

51-53 *By 1867 (see nos. 50 and 51) the pencil had
become a most subtle instrument for Degas.
He might draw very lightly but always with
that sure sense of sculptural form he had
revealed in his earliest drawings. In this head
of an unknown woman (who might be
Mme Loubens; see* LEMOISNE *265, 267) his
strokes model as they curve around her
chignon and behind her neck and hatch
finely under the bridge of her nose. The
color he added to her lips accents the
sensuality which the pencil had already
described in her lowered eyelids and in the
"V" of her dress.*

*That same year he used the pencil delicately,
even caressingly to describe the silken
softness of the baby hair of his niece
Célestine Fevre. She was the daughter of his
sister Marguerite (see no. 2) who in June
1865 had married the architect Henri Fevre
and gave the painter his first nieces and
nephews. Degas drew Célestine, the
first-born, in her parents' apartment on the
boulevard Malesherbes on Christmas Eve
1867 while she listened to the maid tell her a
story as she sat in a nightshirt in the bath. Her
face is not vacuously child-like but absorbed,
even worried, as she listens to the story.*

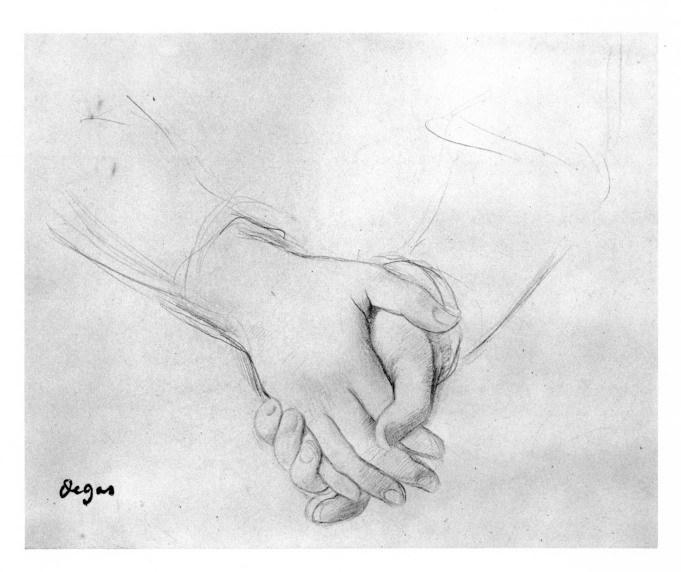

50

Degas's pencil was equally adroit in drawing the infant in no. 53 who could have been the next-born of the Fevre children. He drew with an awareness of the child's cranium, the support of his mother's knee and, again, the softness of his hair. In the second drawing from the top the defenseless sleep seems emphasized by the dark strokes across the child's eyelashes.

51 HEAD OF A WOMAN 1867

VENTE IV: 100d VENTE stamp l.l.
ATELIER stamp *verso* center
Pencil and watercolor
11½ x 8¾ in. (29 x 22 cm.)
Inscription: "Degas 1867" c.r.
Provenance: Vente Atelier Degas IV, July
2-4, 1919, no. 100d; Durand-Ruel;
Olivier Senn
Exhibitions: Paris 1931, no. 115; New York,
Jacques Seligmann, 1960 (November 7-28),
Master Drawings, no. 11
MRS. MURIEL BULTMAN FRANCIS, NEW ORLEANS

52 CELESTINE FEVRE IN HER BATH 1867

Pencil on white paper
7½ x 10¼ in. (19 x 26 cm.)
Inscription: "Ecoutant l'histoire de la bonne
Mimi dans son bain / 24 déc. 67" l.r.
Label: on *verso* "Degas. Portrait de
Célestine Fevre. Morte en Novembre 1908,
à la Colline sur Loup près Nice"
Provenance: the artist to the Fevre family in
1909; Henri Fevre (nephew of the painter)
Literature: Jeanne Fevre, *Mon Oncle Degas,*
Geneva: Pierre Cailler, 1949, p. 112 (not
illustrated); Boggs no. 56
GIANNI AGNELLI, TURIN

53 FOUR STUDIES OF A BABY'S HEAD C. 1867

ATELIER stamp u.l. VENTE stamp *verso*
Pencil on white, light wove paper
12⅝ x 8½ in. (32 x 21.4 cm.)
Provenance: Atelier Degas at time of his
death; Edmond Sagot
THE MINNEAPOLIS INSTITUTE OF ARTS 25.33
*The John de Laittre Memorial Collection,
Gift of Mrs. Horace Ropes*

54 EDOUARD MANET SEATED C. 1865

VENTE II: 210 (2) VENTE stamp l.l.
Study for DELTEIL 15

51

52

Black chalk and estompe on off-white paper
13 x 9⅛ in. (33 x 23 cm.)
Provenance: Vente Atelier Degas II,
December 11-13, 1918, no. 210 (2); bought
by the Metropolitan Museum from the sale,
Seligmann agent
Exhibitions: New London 1936, *Drawings,*
no. 155; Paris 1955, no. 67, pl. 61
Literature: Bryson Burroughs, "Drawings
by Degas," *Metropolitan Museum of Art
Bulletin,* vol. XIV, May 1919, p. 115-116;
Hans Tietze, *European Master Drawings
in the United States,* New York:
J. J. Augustin, 1947, p. 286-287, no. 143;
D. C. Rich, *Edgar Hilaire Germain Degas,*
New York: Abrams, 1951, p. 18; Huyghe
no. 5; Jacob Bean, *100 European Drawings
in the Metropolitan Museum of Art,*
New York: Metropolitan Museum of Art,
1964, no. 74; Longstreet
THE METROPOLITAN MUSEUM OF ART 19.51.7
Rogers Fund 1918

The most important friendship for Degas as
an artist must have been with Edouard
Manet. They were reputed to have met in
the Louvre where both registered as copyists
in 1861 and 1862 (see Theodore Reff,
"Copyists in the Louvre, 1850-1870,"
Art Bulletin, December 1964, pp. 555, 556).
Manet as the more adventurous of the two,
and already notorious in France, must have
encouraged Degas's independence. Both
artists were interested in etching; and Degas
made three etchings of Manet influenced, as
Paul Moses points out (*Etchings by Edgar
Degas,* The Renaissance Society at the
University of Chicago, 1964, no. 13), by the
style of the *Société des Aquafortistes* of
which Manet had been a founding member
in 1862. This meticulous, delicately shaded
drawing was reversed and sharpened in the
etching derived from it. In pencil there is
more of the spontaneous energy Manet
revealed, even seated, and more of a glimmer
of humor in his face.

55 EDOUARD MANET AT THE RACES C. 1870

VENTE II: 210 (3)   VENTE stamp l.l.
Graphite pencil on light brown paper
12⅝ x 9⅝ in. (38 x 24.4 cm.)
Provenance: Vente Atelier Degas II,
December 11-13, 1918, no. 210 (3); bought
by the Metropolitan Museum from that sale,
Seligmann as agent

53

Exhibitions: Minneapolis 1948; Rotterdam & Paris, 1958-59, no. 161 and pl. 157; New York 1959, no. 161
Literature: Mongan p. 65; *European Drawings from the Collection of the Metropolitan Museum of Art*, New York: Metropolitan Museum of Art, 1943, II, pl. 50; Rewald 1946, p. 93, ill. p. 98; Shoolman & Slatkin pl. 102; Boggs no. 43; Alan Bowness, *Impressionists and Post-Impressionists*, New York: Grolier, 1965, p. 62; Longstreet
THE METROPOLITAN MUSEUM OF ART 19.51.8
Rogers Fund 1918

This second drawing of Manet from the Metropolitan Museum reveals another interest he and Degas had in common—the racetrack (see Jean Harris *Art Bulletin*, March 1966, pp. 78-82). In the latter half of the 1860's they presumably visited it frequently together; and both produced pictures from it. This drawing shows Manet distracted by another of his interests—a pretty woman; Degas often drew this particular woman with lorgnettes in different costumes (LEMOISNE 179, 268, 269, 431) and even named her on one of the drawings (LEMOISNE 269) "Lyda." The emphasis here, however, is clearly upon Manet whose stocky, energetic body is revealed by the brusque strokes of a graphite pencil. There is not the same refinement in the description of form as in the other drawing of Manet; its very suggestive abruptness argues for a later date.

56-58 *Degas was inclined to keep at a theme or even at a particular picture, refusing to consider it complete at any stage. One work, which underwent considerable and somewhat confusing repainting, was a racetrack scene (LEMOISNE 184); Benedict Nicolson has chronicled its changes in "The Recovery of a Degas Race Course Scene," Burlington, December 1960, pp. 536-537. An important figure is the principal horse for which no. 56 is probably a study; its anatomical angularity shows Degas's desperate efforts to come to grips with the actual appearance of a horse, regardless of earlier traditions in painting and sculpture. It is, at the same time, nervously proud. Degas also studied the rider, his legs straight and his reins tight in his hands as he brings*

54

Degas

19.51.8

55

*the horse to a halt. Although a jockey in the
collection of Mr. Walter Baker (no. 57) is
stockier and more forceful than the jockey
in any of the transformations on canvas,
he may be a preliminary study for it.
Compared with the gouache drawings of
1866 (no. 46) his effect is one of more
concentrated energy. The spectators in
the painting are Lyda with her lorgnette
(see no. 55) and a male figure who, as he
finally emerged from the cleaning, proved
to have been based on the urbane figure
with an umbrella, Degas's brother Achille
(no. 58). He takes Lyda more for granted
than the inquisitive Manet—but there is a
similar debonnaire eloquence in the way he
stands and wears his clothes.*

56 HORSE AND RIDER 1870-72

VENTE IV: 223 (c) VENTE stamp l.l.
ATELIER stamp l.r.
Study for LEMOISNE 184, 649
Pencil on white paper
11½ x 9 in. (29.2 x 22.9 cm.)
Related Studies: VENTE IV: 231(c), 232
Provenance: Vente Atelier Degas IV, July 2-4
1919, no. 223(c); Durand-Ruel; New Gallery
Exhibitions: Bowdoin College Museum of
Art, *Collecting Privately,* (1964), no. 10,
figure 3

PRIVATE COLLECTION

57 A JOCKEY ON HIS HORSE 1870-72

VENTE III: 128 (2) VENTE stamp l.l.
Study for LEMOISNE 184
Black chalk, brush and gouache on
pink paper
11½ x 6¾ in. (29.2 x 17.2 cm.)
Provenance: Vente Atelier Degas III, April
7-10, 1919, no. 128 (2); Louis Rouart, Paris;
Louis Godefroy, Paris; Franz Koenigs,
Haarlem.
Exhibitions: New York, Metropolitan
Museum of Art, 1960 (June-September),
The Walter C. Baker Collection of Drawings
Literature: Old Master Drawings, v, June
1930, no. 17, p. v, advertisement; Claus
Virch, *Master Drawings in the Collection of
Walter C. Baker,* New York: Metropolitan
Museum of Art, 1962, no. 105

WALTER C. BAKER, NEW YORK

57

56

LEMOISNE 307
Study for LEMOISNE 184
Oil on paper
14½ x 9¼ in. (36.5 x 23.5 cm.)
Provenance: Vente succession de René
de Gas, Hotel Drouot, Paris. November 10,
1927, no. 81; Chester Dale (Sale, Private
Collection, Parke-Bernet, New York,
March 16, 1944, no. 38); Jacques Seligmann
& Co., P. D. McMillan Land Co.,
Minneapolis
Exhibitions: New York, Museum of French
Art, 1929, no. 24; Paris 1931, no. 22;
Cleveland 1947, no. 3; Minneapolis 1948;
Baltimore 1962, no. 37; Santa Barbara
Museum of Art, 1963-64 (December 3-
January 5); New Orleans 1965, p. 63; pl. XVI
Literature: Lemoisne no. 307; *Minneapolis*
Institute of Arts Bulletin, December 1961,
pp. 14-15; Boggs no. 81

THE MINNEAPOLIS INSTITUTE OF ARTS

59 BACK VIEW OF HORSE WITH RIDER 1873

ATELIER stamp l.l.
Study for LEMOISNE 119
Pencil on smooth white paper
8⅞ x 6⅞ in.
Inscription: "35 rue Goujon" u.c.
Related Study: Louvre RF 12.276
Provenance: Marcel Guérin, Paris
(his stamp l.l.)
Exhibitions: London, Leicester Galleries,
1963, *Artists as Collectors*, no. 109

MR. AND MRS. ELIOT HODGKIN, LONDON

Since Degas's racetrack and riding studies
are not easy to date it is pleasant to be
given a clue to their chronology. This
drawing of a horseman is very close to
gouache in the Louvre (RF 12.276) of a
gentleman rider in a red coat; in the lower
corner of the gouache there is the pencil
inscription with the form of the name the
painter used earlier in his life, "De Gas 73."
Both drawings were studies for a group of
hunters in a painting called *Le Départ pour*
la Chasse (LEMOISNE 119). Degas was
inclined to concentrate upon either the horse
or the rider. In the Louvre drawing it is the
colorfully clad solid back of the rider; the
horse is somewhat inadequate under him.
Here, on the other hand, the emphasis is
upon the subtly drawn animal—so

58

magnificent and fully realized when compared with the shy and endearing dobbin Degas had drawn a decade earlier (no. 42).

60 HORSE C. 1873

VENTE IV: 209b VENTE stamp l.l.
Study for LEMOISNE 119
Pencil on white paper
9 x 11¾ in. (22.9 x 29.9 cm.)
Related Study: VENTE IV: 209a
Provenance: Vente Atelier Degas IV, July 2-4, 1919, no. 209b; Davis; A. Conger Goodyear, purchased from Scott and Fowles, New York, February, 1923
Exhibitions: Buffalo, Albright Art Gallery, 1923 (October); New York Century Club, 1938 (April); Oakland, Mills College, 1939 (February-March); Seattle Art Museum, 1939 (April-May); Buffalo, Albright Art Gallery, 1939 (December); Buffalo, Albright-Knox Art Gallery, 1966 (April 30-June 5), *Paintings, Sculpture, Drawings and Prints Collected by A. Conger Goodyear,* no. 105
MRS. ALDO B. BERTOZZI, BUFFALO

In composing *Le Départ pour la Chasse* Degas decided to have a hunter mounting a fully-developed horse at the right of the painting. It is quite possible he did something he was to do often later in his life—turn to a drawing he had already made (in this case, of a saddle horse in black chalk now in the Winthrop Collection at the Fogg Art Museum), make an impression of it, and strengthen that mirror-image with pencil into the drawing we have here; it was now in the right direction for his composition. Both drawings are so descriptive they might be anatomical studies of the horse and both, unlike no. 59, suggest the color and luster of the horse's coat. The extreme difference in style between this drawing and no. 59, does not, in itself, argue for different dates; they were studies in which quite different problems were examined.

61 YOUNG WOMAN HALF-DRESSED, *Study for Le Viol* 1868-72

VENTE III: 23
LEMOISNE 351

59

Study for LEMOISNE 348
Oil on ochre paper applied to canvas
paper 24 x 19¼ in. (61 x 50 cm.); Drawing
18½ x 11¹³⁄₁₆ (47 x 30 cm.)
Provenance: Vente Atelier Degas III, April
7-9, no. 23; Collection x . . . , Frankfurt
(anonymous sale, Frankfurt, October 17,
1928, no. 55) Dr. Hermann Ganz, Zurich
Exhibitions: Amsterdam 1952, no. 12
Literature: Rivière no. 78; Lemoisne 351;
Leymarie no. 22; Pecírka no. 26
Related Literature: Jean Adhémar, *Emile
Zola,* Paris: Bibliothèque Nationale, 1952,
nos. 114, 114a

OEFFENTLICHE KUNSTSAMMLUNG BASEL

One of Degas's most dramatic compositions
was the painting with the bewildering
subject and title of *Le Viol,* in which a man
and a semi-dressed woman are seen in a
bedroom which is constructed with the
calculation of a set on a stage. The
preparatory studies, among them LEMOISNE
353 and BN 8, pp. 99, 100, add to the
painting's fascination. It was M. Jean
Adhémar who identified *Le Viol* as a scene
from Emile Zola's *Madeleine Férat* which
was published in 1868. Although it is
not impossible that Degas quite
characteristically telescoped several episodes
from the novel into the final painting, it
seems closest to the terrible night Madeleine
and her husband Guillaume spent up in
the bedroom of their cottage near [sic]
Véteuil after she had confessed that she
had been his closest friend's mistress before
she met her husband. Zola writes that she
had slipped on a peignoir which she let fall
open absent-mindedly as she sat stunned
before the fire.

Although the drawing in the exhibition
was not used in the final version of the
painting it is certainly related to it. The
semi-nude figure is rendered in oil on the
dark paper with the "challenging
sensuality," the "powerful nudity," which
so disturbed Guillaume that night. It could
illustrate the scene where "Madeleine
laissa tomber le tisonnier. Elle se renversa
dans le fauteuil, cachant son dos, découvrant
sa poitrine. Elle garda son silence, sa face
morne." At the same time Degas was
reticent enough about her plight to add
paper around his original sheet so that there

61

60

would seem to be more space between
her and the spectator.

62 A YOUNG WOMAN IN STREET COSTUME C. 1872

LEMOISNE 296
Brush with transparent black wash and
opaque black and white body color on
rose-beige paper
12¾ x 9⅞ in. (32.5 x 25 cm.)
Inscription: "Degas" l.r. in blue
Provenance: Durand-Ruel; Paul J. Sachs
1927; bequest of Meta and Paul J. Sachs to
the Fogg Art Museum 1965
Exhibitions: Cambridge 1929, no. 33;
St. Louis 1932; Northampton 1933, no. 26;
Boston 1935, no. 122; Philadelphia 1936,
no. 76; Brooklyn 1939; Washington, Phillips
Memorial Gallery, 1940, *Modern Drawings;*
Detroit 1941, no. 22; Boston Institute of
Modern Art, 1943 (November), *France
Forever;* Wellesley 1946; Cleveland 1947,
no. 66; Washington 1947, no. 32; New York
1947; Williamstown, Lawrence Museum,
1948 (November); New York 1949, no. 24;
Richmond 1952; Boston, Institute of
Contemporary Art, 1955 (January &
February), *The Pleasures of Collecting;*
Paris 1955, no. 70; Chicago 1955-56, no. 151;
Los Angeles 1958, no. 19; New York 1960,
no. 81; Baltimore 1962, no. 36; Cambridge
1965 and New York 1966-67, no. 58
Literature: Vingt Dessins pl. 11; Mongan &
Sachs no. 669; Lemoisne 296; Huyghe &
Jacottet, pl. 95, Klaus Berger,
*Französische Meisterzeichnungen des XIX
Jahrhunderts,* Basel, 1949, no. 41; Shoolman
& Slatkin p. 178, pl. 101; Huyghe no. 8

FOGG ART MUSEUM 1965.260
Bequest of Meta and Paul J. Sachs

Shown only at Philadelphia Museum of Art
and the Minneapolis Institute of Arts
In this magnificent gouache drawing Degas
used the human body and the costume as
instruments in addition to his brush. This
unknown woman lifts and turns her head on
her rather frail shoulders with consummate
pride as if such spirit were necessary to
balance her fashionable and extravagant
bustle. Degas, with his sure compositional
instinct, placed her toward the left of the
page, her body forming a straight diagonal
as it turns toward the space in which, with
dignity, it will move.

62

63 STUDY OF THE BALLET FROM MEYERBEER'S OPERA,
Robert le Diable 1872

VENTE III: 363(2) VENTE stamp l.l.
Study for LEMOISNE 294
Sepia ink on cream paper
11 x 17 in. (27 x 42 cm.)
Provenance: Vente Atelier Degas III, April
7-9, 1919, no. 364 (1); bought by the
Victoria and Albert Museum at that sale,
Knoedler as agent.
Literature: Browse, no. 6a

VICTORIA AND ALBERT MUSEUM, LONDON

Degas's interest in the theater was
instinctive. It is apparent from his
enthusiasm for the *théâtre des italiens* in
Paris as early as 1855 (BN 10). Family
archives in New Orleans, where his mother
was born, and Naples, where his father was,
show that it was a family enthusiasm, his
American cousins interested in the Mardi
Gras, the Italians in the Opera. By 1872
Degas's own preoccupation was the ballet
which he studied in performance and
rehearsal at the opera house on the rue le
Peletier, while the present *Opéra*, which was
to replace it, was under construction. It was
there, toward the end of 1871, that
Meyerbeer's opera, *Robert le Diable*, was
revived. Degas recorded its Ballet of the
Nuns against a gas-lit, cloistered set and
above a double row of inattentive male
spectators, dating the first of his versions of
this subject 1872.

64 STUDY OF THE BALLET FROM MEYERBEER'S OPERA,
Robert le Diable 1872

VENTE III: 364 (2) VENTE stamp l.l.
Study for LEMOISNE 294
Sepia ink on cream paper
11 x 17 in. (27 x 42 cm.)
Provenance: Vente Atelier Degas III, April
7-9, 1919, no. 364 (2); bought by the
Victoria and Albert Museum at that sale
Literature: Browse no. 6

VICTORIA AND ALBERT MUSEUM; LONDON

Although Degas did study the elaborate set
for the Ballet of the Nuns in a notebook
(BN 22, pp. 13, 15, 17), the four known
independent drawings are devoted to the
dancers. They are the spirit of nuns who
have been guilty of carnal sin and who,
having been resurrected from the dead,
dance in the cloister, finally shedding their

63

64

habits to reveal their sensual natures. Degas drew (and painted) them moving slowly, but with the suggestion of their desire to be free of their cumbersome and even shroud-like robes. Since so little articulation was possible with the simple garments, Degas's strokes of the brush were broad and direct. In the sepia color of the ink, the dryness of the ink on the brush, and in their expressive harmony, these drawings suggest the influence of Rembrandt or other 17th century draughtsmen.

65-66 *Degas quickly made himself as much at home in the rehearsals and classes of the ballet at the* Opéra *as he did at the performances themselves. As Mr. Pickvance has documented (Burlington, June 1963, p. 257) one of the first works Degas sold to the dealer Durand-Ruel was* La Leçon de Danse à l'Opéra de la rue Le Peletier (LEMOISNE 298) *which was exhibited in London late in 1872. At such dancing classes the crucial figure was the* maître de ballet de l'Opéra *who in 1872 was Louis François Mérante, at that time forty-four years old (BROWSE p. 53). Although he is by no means clearly identifiable the two Chicago drawings of the back of a* maître *or* professeur de ballet *suggest something of the stance of M. Mérante in the finished* La Leçon de Danse. *The pencil version (no. 65), which is more developed and serious, was squared for transferral although we know nothing produced from it. It gives a remarkable impression of a sturdy, bandy-legged body under loose, misshapen clothes. The gouache version, although seductive in color, runs close to broad caricature, but a caricature in which pathos rather than malice is combined with comedy.*

65 THE BALLET MASTER C. 1872

VENTE IV: 206a VENTE stamp l.l.
ATELIER stamp l.r.
Pencil and chalk with estompe
16⅛ x 11⅝ in. (40.8 x 29.6 cm.)
Provenance: Vente Atelier Degas IV, July 2-4, 1919, no. 206a
THE ART INSTITUTE OF CHICAGO 51.110a

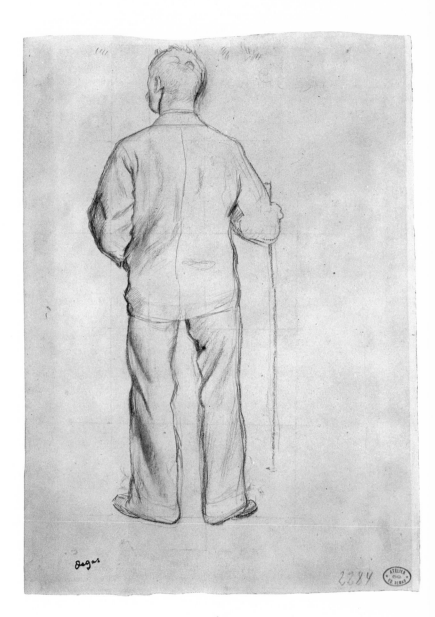

65

66

66 THE BALLET MASTER C. 1872

VENTE IV: 206b VENTE stamp l.l.
Watercolor or gouache and oil over black
crayon and pen
17¾ x 10¼ in. (45 x 26 cm.)
*Provenance: Vente Atelier Degas IV, July
2-4, 1919, no. 206b*
Literature: Browse no. 40a

THE ART INSTITUTE OF CHICAGO 51.110b

67 HEADS OF MEN C. 1872

VENTE IV: 132e VENTE stamp l.r.
Pencil on white paper
14⅛ x 9 in. (36 x 23 cm.)
Related Drawings: VENTE IV: 131a; 132a-d
*Provenance: Vente Atelier Degas IV, July
2-4, 1919, no. 132e;* G. Viau; F. Koenigs;
given by D. G. van Beuningen 1940
Exhibitions: Basel 1935, no. 154; Amsterdam
1946, no. 63; Bern 1951/52, no. 165
Literature: Longstreet

MUSEUM BOYMANS-VAN BEUNINGEN,
ROTTERDAM F11.130

Among the contents of Degas's studio were
two sheets of heads of different men, placed
presumably at random on the page. The
heads on the sheet not in the exhibition
(VENTE IV: 131a) have been identified as
those of Napoleon III and his field marshalls
at the time of the Franco-Prussian War; it
was probably based upon the illustrations in
the daily press which Degas considerably
animated in his own versions. The man in
this drawing—four of them, one repeated at
the top three times—remain tantalizingly
anonymous although the figure in the smock
at the left *could* be Degas himself. These are
quick pencil drawings with considerable
expressive range.

68 MATHILDE MUSSON BELL 1872

Study for LEMOISNE 318
Pencil and colored crayon
12½ x 9½ in. (31 x 24 cm.)
Inscription: "Nouvelle Orléans 72 /
Degas" l.r.
Provenance: Jeanne Fevre; Mme Guillaume
Walter, Paris; John Rewald (Sale Sotheby's,
London, July 7, 1960, no. 25)
Exhibitions: East Hampton, L. I., 1952,
Influences in French Painting, no. 29;
Montreal Museum of Fine Arts, 1953,

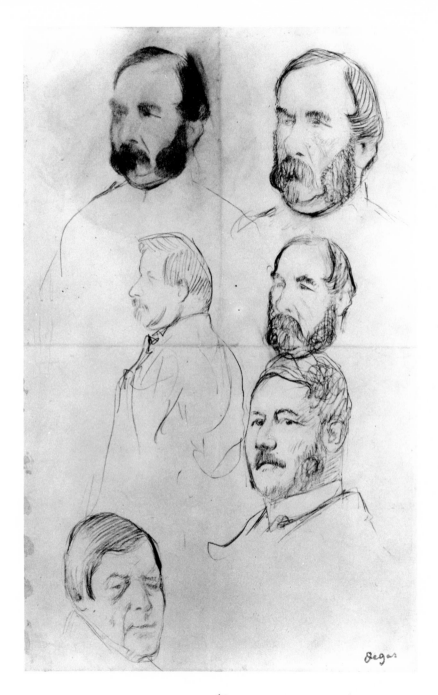

67

Five Centuries of Drawings, no. 205;
New York 1958, no. 12, pl. VII; New York
1960, no. 82; New York, Charles E. Slatkin,
1961 (December and January), *The Artist
as Draughtsman,* no. 48 and cover
New Orleans 1965, p. 47, pl. VII
Literature: Rewald 1961, p. 277; Boggs
p. 109
MR. AND MRS. RICHARD L. SELLE, CHICAGO

Although Degas does not seem to have
spent more than three months in New
Orleans the winter of 1872-73 and although
he complained in his letters back to France
of his inability to work because of his
eyesight, he was surprisingly productive
making family portraits and his remarkable
group portrait, *The Cotton Market.* The
sitter for this drawing was probably his
cousin Mathilde Musson who was married
to William Bell; her eyes are too animated
to be her sister (the painter's sister-in-law)
for Estelle Musson de Gas was blind. The
drawing has a flavour of New Orleans in
the pretty, dotted dress of some thin material
the palm fan, the suggestion of light, the
nearly coquettish way in which Mathilde
Bell looks up at us, and even in the very
languor of the lines.

69 JOSEPHINE GAUJELIN, DANCER 1873

VENTE III: 156 (1) VENTE stamp l.r.
Pencil on white paper
12 x 8 in. (30 x 19 cm.)
Inscription: "1873 / Josephine Gaujelin /
autrefois danseuse à l'Opéra / puis actrice
au Gymnase"
Provenance: Vente Atelier Degas III, April
7-9, 1919, no. 156 (1); Durand-Ruel;
Kelekian; F. Koenigs; given by D. G. van
Beuningen 1940
Exhibitions: Rotterdam 1933-34, no. 49;
Basel 1935, no. 155
Literature: Browse no. 12; Longstreet
MUSEUM BOYMANS-VAN BEUNINGEN,
ROTTERDAM F11.169

The dancers in Degas's drawings and
paintings are difficult to identify (see
Browse p. 60). One reason may be that the
finished works were a combination of
studies at the Opera House itself and others
made from models in his studio. Since her
name does not appear on the roster of the
Opera House and since she had already sat

68

for a portrait which Degas exhibited at the Salon of 1869 (LEMOISNE 165), Josephine Gaujelin must have been such a model; indeed Degas inscribed this drawing helpfully "Josephine Gaujelin autrefois danseuse à l'Opéra/puis actrice au Gymnase." He also wrote on another gouache drawing of her in the *tutu* of the ballerina, "D'après Gaujelin 1873." He could use the aging former dancer (with the strong eyebrows which still link her to the portrait exhibited in 1869) to study the conventional positions of the dance. In this chaste and spiritedly accented pencil drawing, his interest in the balance of the figure is apparent in the two vertical lines he drew up from the foot on which her weight rests.

70 A BALLET DANCER IN POSITION 1874

VENTE I: 328
Study for LEMOISNE 340
Pencil with crayon and white chalk on pink paper
16⅛ x 11¼ in. (41 x 28.5 cm.)
Inscription: "Degas" l.r.
Provenance: Vente Atelier Degas I, May 6-8, 1918, no. 328; Fevre; César de Hauke to Paul J. Sachs 1929; bequest of Meta and Paul J. Sachs 1965
Exhibitions: New York 1930, no. 34; Cambridge 1931, no. 32; St. Louis 1932; Buffalo 1935, no. 116; Boston 1935, no. 118; Philadelphia 1936, no. 75; Paris 1937, no. 81; Boston, Museum of Modern Art, 1938, *The Ballet in Art*; Brooklyn 1939; Washington 1940; San Francisco 1940, *Master Drawings*, no. 19; Detroit 1941, no. 23; Richmond, Virginia Museum of Arts, 1944 (January-February), *19th Century French Painting*, no. 24; New York 1945, no. 63; New York, Century Club, 1947; Philadelphia Museum of Art, 1950-51 (November 4-February 11), *Masterpieces of Drawing*, no. 95; Richmond 1952; San Antonio 1955; Rotterdam & Paris, 1958-59, no. 166; New York 1959, no. 166; Cambridge 1964-65, & New York 1966-67, no. 59
Literature: Vingt Dessins pl. 10; Jamot p. 135, pl. 18; P. Jamot, *La Peinture au Musée du Louvre: Ecole française*, 1929, pt. 3, p. 64; Mongan & Sachs no. 670; Browse no. 10; Sachs p. 106, pl. 64; Huyghe & Jaccottet,

69

70

p. 175, pl. 92; Huttinger p. 43; Moskowitz & Mongan no. 781
FOGG ART MUSEUM 1965.263
Bequest of Meta and Paul J. Sachs
Shown only at Philadelphia Museum of Art and The Minneapolis Institute of Arts

A dancer, who was younger and prettier than Josephine Gaujelin (see no. 69), posed for some of Degas's drawings in the early 1870s which were squared for transferral to finished works. Her large, expressive mouth and long, turned-up nose suggest she may have been a younger, plumper Mlle Malo whose portrait Degas was to paint and draw some five years later (see LEMOISNE 441-444); Mlle Malo was a dancer of no great reputation (and therefore probably available as a model) whom Degas mentioned in a letter from New Orleans the winter of 1872 (see Lettres p. 17). In this drawing the pencil and the touches of white on the pink paper seem to express Degas's pleasure in the buoyancy of the curved arms, in the rounded breasts and the deftly pointed toe of the young dancer. Although a figure in a similar position appears in the *Rehearsal of the Ballet on the Stage* (LEMOISNE 400) which Pickvance (*Burlington*, June 1963, p. 260) shows as first conceived as a pencil drawing for the *Illustrated London News* in 1873, it is more likely that this drawing was made for the reworking of that version in essence or for a grisaille oil (LEMOISNE 340) which was exhibited in the Impressionist exhibition in 1874.

71 DANCER ADJUSTING SLIPPER 1874

Study for LEMOISNE 343
Graphite pencil and charcoal heightened with white chalk on faded pink paper
12⅞ x 9⅝ in. (33 x 24.4 cm.)
Inscription: "Degas" l.l.; "le bras est enfoncé un peu dans la mousseline" r.c.
Provenance: H. O. Havemeyer Collection
Exhibitions: New York, The Metropolitan Museum 1930, *The H. O. Havemeyer Collection*, no. 160; Washington 1947, no. 33; San Antonio 1955; New York 1960, no. 84
Literature: W. Mehring, *Degas*, New York: Herrman, 1944, no. 25; Browse no. 20; Shoolman & Slatkin no. 105; Huyghe no. 31; The Metropolitan Museum, *The H. O.*

Degas

Le bras est enfoncé dans
un faux la
moustache

71

Havemeyer Collection, New York: 1958,
p. 24, no. 131; Rosenberg no. 206;
Longstreet

THE METROPOLITAN MUSEUM OF ART
29.100.941
Bequest of Mrs. H. O. Havemeyer 1929

The same model as no. 70 posed for *The
Dancer Adjusting her Slipper.* We find the
same bracelets, the same ribbon around her
neck, the same hair and the same rounded
breasts; both are drawn with pencil and
white chalk on pink paper (now faded)
which has been squared for transferral. She
is a study for a composition (LEMOISNE 343)
which Degas dated 1874. Characteristically
for this period, this ballerina is in a position
which exerts considerable pressure upon
different parts of her body, but is in no sense
involved in the movements of a dance. Its
very informality is appropriate for the year
in which Impressionism was born. Degas
wrote on the edge of this drawing his
observation that "the arm sinks a little into
the gauze."

72 THE DANCER JULES PERROT 1875

VENTE III: 67 VENTE stamp l.l.
LEMOISNE 367
Study for LEMOISNE 366
Pastel on blue paper
24⅝ x 17¾ in. (62.5 x 45 cm.)
Related Studies: VENTE III: 157(3)
Provenance: Vente Atelier Degas III, April
7-9, no. 67; G. Pellet; M. Exsteens
Exhibitions: Bern, Klipstein und Kornfeld,
1960 (October 22-November 30), *Choix
d'une collection privée: Sammlungen G. P.
und M. E.,* no. 10; Laren, Singer Memorial
Foundation, 1964 (July 4-September 16),
La Belle Epoque, no. 12, pl. 5
Literature: M.-L. Bataille, "Degas," *Kunst
und Kunstler,* July 1930, p. 407; Lemoisne
367

MESSRS. E. J. VAN WISSELINGH & CO.,
AMSTERDAM

One of the great figures from the era of the
Romantic ballet Degas knew was the male
dancer, Jules Perrot, who retired after he
returned from Russia in 1859 but would give
occasional classes. When Perrot, who was
born in 1810, was about sixty-five Degas
recorded two such classes (LEMOISNE 341,
397) and one picture of him at rehearsal

72

(LEMOISNE 365); he also painted a portrait of the retired dancer (LEMOISNE 366). If this pastel head of Pagans could not be identified by its clear relationship to a drawing of Pagans seated [VENTE III: 157(1)] which is inscribed "le danseur Perrot," its weary features could be easily recognized from contemporary photographs. Inactive, as he is here, all the animation has gone out of Perrot's body and face and all the consequences of age have appeared. Degas was using his pastel and chalk lightly but with increasing dependence upon its color, as we discover in Perrot's glowing face.

73 THE DANCER, JULES PERROT 1875

LEMOISNE 364
Study for LEMOISNE 341, 397 and 366
Essence on gray-green paper
18¾ x 11¾ in. (47.5 x 30 cm.)
Inscription: "Degas / 1875" l.r.
Related Studies: VENTE III: 157 (2)
Provenance: M. Exsteens, Petitdidier; Fernand Ochsé; Paul Brame; César de Hauke
Exhibitions: Copenhagen 1914, *Art français*, no. 703; Paris 1924, no. 54; Northampton 1933, no. 22; Cambridge 1934, no. 20; Buffalo 1935, no. 117; Philadelphia 1936, no. 78; Cleveland 1947, no. 67
Literature: Rivière pl. 26; Browse no. 24; Lemoisne 364; Rosenberg no. 214; Boggs no. 93; Pecírka pl. 28

HENRY P. MCILHENNY, PHILADELPHIA
Shown only at Philadelphia Museum of Art

Although the effects of age are apparent in this standing figure of Perrot, his hair white, his shoulder curved, his body heavy, there is the suggestion of purpose behind his actions which we know from related paintings is the critical observation of the performance of dancers at classes and in rehearsal. Degas, who himself observed the movements of all bodies as critically as Perrot did those of the dancers, saw expressive possibilities in the combination of inertia and sense of authority to be conveyed by Perrot's own body. And once more he felt that dress— here comfortably loose but glowingly luminous—provided another dimension to the interpretation of a human being. How much more easily Degas was working can be seen by comparing this with the *maître de*

73

ballet in nos. 65 and 66, probably drawn three years earlier.

74 STUDY OF BALLERINA C. 1876

VENTE II: 326 VENTE stamp l.l.
Study for LEMOISNE 397 or LEMOISNE 341
Charcoal, heightened with white, on
buff paper
19¼ x 11¾ in. (49 x 30 cm.)
Variant of: VENTE II: 332
Provenance: Vente Atelier Degas II,
December 11-13, 1918, no. 326; Thomas
Couper, Glasgow; Mr. and Mrs. Samuel
Sair, Winnipeg (Sold Park-Bernet,
December 9, 1959, no. 27)
Exhibitions: New York 1958, no. 22, pl. XVI
Literature: Browse p. 342, no. 19 (not ill'd)

CHARLES E. SLATKIN INC. GALLERIES, NEW YORK

As Degas watched the rehearsals at the
Opera House, which in 1875 were
transferred to the new building by Garnier,
he took great pleasure in recording the
positions and movements of the dancers at
rest. As Miss Browse has pointed out
(Browse p. 59) these were never absolutely
unself-conscious or relaxed; even when this
dancer adjusted her bodice and cockily
fluffed out her skirt, she was knowingly
controlling the movement of her body; her
feet quite naturally fell into a conventional
ballet position. This drawing, which was in
looser, freer and faster charcoal and chalk,
may have been one of the studies leading up
to the *Dancing Class with M. Perrot*
(LEMOISNE 341; see no. 73) but more
probably the source is a drawing in the
Detroit Institute of Arts (VENTE II: 332) in
pencil and chalk on white paper. The
lowered bodice and shortened skirt of this
dancer argue that she was conceived, if not
used, for the 1876 version of the *Dancing
Class with M. Perrot* (LEMOISNE 397).

75 DANCER WITH A FAN C. 1876

Pencil with chalk on bistre paper
18½ x 11⅜ in. (47 x 29 cm.)
Inscription: "à mon ami Duret / Degas" u.r.
Provenance: Théodore Duret; his gift to the
museum in 1908
Exhibitions: Bern, La Chaux de Fonds,
Geneva, Basel, 1947, *Quelques oeuvres des
collections de la Ville de Paris,* no. 20;

74

75

Zurich, Kunsthaus, 1947, *Le Petit Palais*,
no. 203; Vienna, Albertina, 1950, *Meister-*
werke aus Frankreichs Museen, no. 235;
Rotterdam, Boymans, 1952-53, *Franse*
meesters uit het Petit Palais, no. 42; Paris
1955, no. 90, ill. p. 56
Literature: Florent Fels, "Monsieur Duret,"
Le Jardin des Arts, no. 107, October 1963,
reproduced p. 27
MUSEE DU PETIT PALAIS, PARIS

Degas generally tried to suppress his instinct
for characterization in his studies from the
ballet. It broke out in this *Dancer with the*
Fan and also in a related drawing in the
Boymans-Van Beuningen Museum in
Rotterdam (VENTE III: 339(1)) which is the
same size but crisper in its draughtsmanship,
in the contours of the skirt and even in the
position of the body; but in both the sense
of the comic and the wistfully unhappy are
combined. In the Petit Palais drawing the
dancer's position seems automatic but
weary, her skirt limp and her fan protective
rather than provocative, but she does hold
her head back valiantly. It takes the softness
of the transition from charcoal to white
chalk to suggest this range in
psychological mood.

76 FOUR STUDIES OF GROOMS C. 1875-77

VENTE III: 37(1) VENTE stamp l.r.
LEMOISNE 383
Essence on oiled brown paper
15⅜ x 9½ in. (39 x 24 cm.)
Related Studies: no. 77; LEMOISNE 383bis;
VENTE IV: 237e
Provenance: Vente Atelier Degas III, April
7-9, 1919, no. 37(1); Nunès et Fiquet
Literature: Lemoisne 383
MRS. MARIANNE FEILCHENFELDT, ZURICH

In the mid-1870's Degas occasionally
deserted the world of Paris theatres. Just as
he was more interested in the rehearsals and
classes of the Opera ballet than in the
performance, in his few racetrack pictures
at that time he showed a similar concern for
the preparations rather than for the race
itself. It was characteristic that he should
have made four brush studies of the grooms
who tended the horses, their ill-fitting,
brown suits, buttoned at the neck, and
bowler hats intentionally understated when
compared with the brilliant silks of the

76

77

jockeys (no. 46) a decade or so earlier. Although the grooms ride, it seems from necessity and habit rather than in anticipation of the excitement of the race. Their colorless role at the racetrack is emphasized by the brown essence which has been partly absorbed by the oiled brown paper; only the ink drawing and a touch or two of white gouache stand out against it.

77 TWO STUDIES OF A GROOM 1875-77

VENTE III: 153 (2) VENTE stamp l.l
LEMOISNE 382
Brown essence, heightened with gouache, on ochre paper
9⅞ x 13½ in. (25 x 34.2 cm.)
Provenance: Vente Atelier Degas III, April 7-9 1919, no. 153 (2); acquired by Marcel Bing; his legacy to the Louvre 1922
Exhibitions: Paris 1924, no. 92; Bucharest, Muzeul Toma Stelian, 1931 (November 8-December 15), *Desenul francez*, no. 103; Paris, Cabinet des Dessins du Musée du Louvre, 1964, *Dessins de sculpteurs de Pajou à Rodin*, no. 73
Literature: Rivière pl. 16; Lafond vol. I, p. 44; Jamot pl. 30; M. Rebatet, *Degas,* Paris: Bibliothèque Française des Arts, 1944, pl. 52; Lemoisne no. 382; Cooper no. 3; Pecírka no. 9

CABINET DES DESSINS DU MUSEE DU LOUVRE
RF 5601
Shown only at City Art Museum of Saint Louis

In drawing the grooms, Degas found that although one figure, at the right in this drawing, might prosaically twist to dismount, another could be involved in a dramatic action—reining in a horse that is straining to bolt away. The situation is ignoble, the horse ugly in its desperation, the rider efficient but puny. Nevertheless, in the visual conflict between the dark mass of the rider against the white diagonal of the horse (the two tied together by the reins), there is considerable force which the strong lines of india ink and the contrast between darks and lights intensify.

78-80 *In the late 1870s Degas began to make pencil notations of the jockeys themselves as they relaxed between races. Occasionally a rider would have to rein in a horse (no. 78)—but*

Degas

78

*more gracefully than the groom in no. 77;
Degas's pencil had to move quickly and
somewhat loosely to record the action. It
could work more slowly and more firmly
with the quieter figure of the jockey in no. 79
where the faint moustache and the color of
the jacket are described by the precise
pencil line. At times Degas was inclined to
carry the drawing even further as he was in
no. 80, probably with the intention of
incorporating it into a finished painting. He
blurred the pencil with his estompe to
indicate color in the jacket and also its shine,
he described the buttons delicately, and the
hands, which hold the reins lightly, firmly.
He characterized the head more exactly with
its receding (if solid) chin, the enormous
moustaches, unhappy mouth and small,
unfocused eyes. Something of the sense of
isolation in this drawing of a jockey is
maintained in the painting for which it was
probably a study (LEMOISNE 649) and which
also incorporated an earlier drawing of a
horse (no. 56).*

78 JOCKEY 1878

VENTE III: 128 (1) VENTE stamp l.l.
Study for LEMOISNE 387 or LEMOISNE 461
Pencil on light gray paper
12¾ x 9⅝ in. (32.5 x 24.4 cm.)
Related Studies: VENTE IV: 274
Provenance: Vente Atelier Degas III,
April 7-9, 1919, no. 128 (1); Louis Rouart;
Franz Koenigs; Zurich dealer
Exhibitions: Amsterdam 1938, no. 54;
Exhibitions of *Collection of John S.
Newberry:* Fogg Art Museum, Cambridge,
1960, no. 7; Museum of Fine Arts, Boston,
1962, no. 36
*Literature: The John S. Newberry
Collection,* The Detroit Institute of Arts,
Detroit 1965, pp. 30-31
THE DETROIT INSTITUTE OF ARTS 65.147
John S. Newberry Bequest

79 THE JOCKEY 1878

VENTE IV: 260a VENTE stamp l.l.
Pencil on off-white, rough, straw-flecked
paper
12½ x 9½ in. (31 x 24 cm.)
Inscription: dated "1878" *verso*
Related Studies: VENTE III: 92 (1); VENTE IV;
218a

79

80

Provenance: Vente Atelier Degas IV, July
2-4 1919, no. 260a; Albert S. Henraux, Paris
Exhibitions: New York 1958, no. 29, pl. XXIII
WILLIAM S. PALEY, NEW YORK

80 JOCKEY C.1878-80

VENTE IV: 215b VENTE stamp l.l.
Study for LEMOISNE 649
Pencil
12¾ x 9½ in. (32.3 x 24.2 cm.)
Provenance: Vente Atelier Degas IV, July
2-4, 1919, no. 215b; Durand-Ruel

THE ART INSTITUTE OF CHICAGO 22.5518
Gift of Robert Allerton

81 *Study for* LA CHANSON DU CHIEN C. 1877

VENTE III: 305 VENTE stamp l.l.
Study for LEMOISNE 380 and DELTEIL 48
Pencil on white paper
15⅜ x 9⅞ in. (39 x 25 cm.)
Provenance: Vente Atelier Degas III, April
7-9, 1919, no. 305

CHARLES DURAND-RUEL, PARIS

Degas, along with Renoir and Manet,
enjoyed the café-concerts of Paris where,
on stages built out-of-doors, singers
performed on gas-lit summer nights. Unlike
Renoir who at the same time showed
customers enjoying themselves dancing at
the *Moulin de la Galette*, Degas was, as
always, interested in the professional
performance. His pleasure in this singer
must have been one he shared with his
friend, the playwright and librettist, Ludovic
Halévy, because in a notebook in which
he used to draw at the Halévy's he made
several drawings of her (Daniel Halévy,
Album de Dessins de Degas, Paris: Quatre
Chemins-Editart, 1949), in one of them
carrying her to grotesque caricature,
pointing her ears, widening her mouth and
exaggerating the size of her teeth. The
drawing here is conventional in preparation
for the lithograph and painting which
were made from it. With pencil Degas
indicated the bulk of her figure, her dress
and her coiffure, and emphasized her arms
and hands in the gesture which grew out
of her song, the Song of the Dog.

81

82

82 TWO STUDIES FOR A MUSIC HALL SINGER
   1878-80

LEMOISNE 504
Pastel and charcoal on gray paper
20½ x 25 in. (52 x 63 cm.)
Inscription: "Degas" l.l.
Provenance: Boussod and Valadon, Paris;
Albert S. Henraux, Paris; Paul Rosenberg
Exhibitions: Paris 1924, no. 166; Paris,
Galerie Paul Rosenberg, 1932, *Dessins et
Pastels de Degas*, no. 31; Paris, Bernheim
Jeune, 1936 (May 25-July 13), *Cent ans de
théâtre*, no. 26; Paris 1937, no. 116; Los
Angeles 1958, no. 31; San Francisco and
Santa Barbara 1966, *The Collection of Mrs.
John Wintersteen*, no. 5
Literature: Rivière no. 90, Grappe;
Lemoisne 504; Cooper no. 13; J. Canaday,
Mainstreams of Modern Art, no. 233,
pl. 198; Pecírka no. 46; Rosenberg no. 224

MRS. JOHN WINTERSTEEN, PHILADELPHIA
Shown only at City Art Museum of
Saint Louis

Of all Degas's café-concert singers the most
absorbed and the most eloquent are the two
in this pastel. It is possible that Degas made
two studies of one singer on the same page
but since he used two figures in the same
costume on two other occasions (LEMOISNE
505 and 506) and in one case (LEMOISNE 505)
in a pastel developed to the point of a
painting, it seems likely that he was
recording a duet. Degas drew the singer at
the left, as he did in another drawing (VENTE
III: 335(1)), with bold lines of charcoal
which expose her powerfully expressive
arms as she lifts her shoulders, transported
by her song. The singer at the right,
although she imitates the other's gestures,
is handled more tenderly. She is fully and
prettily dressed, the emphasis upon her
curved hands rather than her arms, her
gentle face radiant as she sings; the color of
the pastel enhances her glow. The twisting
in space from one figure to the other, with
its change in emphasis, seems to fill the
drawing with their song.

83 MISS LALA AT THE CIRQUE FERNANDO
   January 25, 1879

VENTE IV: 255a VENTE stamp l.l.
Study for LEMOISNE 522
Black chalk and pastel on coarse,
yellowish paper

83

18½ x 12½ in. (47 x 32 cm.)
Inscription: "Miss Lala / 25 janvier 79" u.l.
Related Studies: LEMOISNE 525; VENTE IV:
256a, b, c; LEMOISNE 524, 523; Daniel Halévy,
Album de Dessins de Degas, Paris: Quatre
Chemins-Editart, 1949, p. 97
Provenance: Vente Atelier Degas IV, July
2-4, 1919, no. 255a; Dr. Georges Viau;
Jacques Seligmann & Co., Agnew; bought
by the Barber Institute from Agnew 1936
Exhibitions: Cambridge 1931, no. 19a;
London, Matthiesen, 1938, *A Century of
French Drawings,* no. 44; London, British
Institute of Adult Education, *Nineteenth
Century French Drawings,* no. 13
Literature: Rivière pl. 38; *Handbook of the
Barber Institute of Fine Arts,* Birmingham,
1949, p. 19; *Catalogue of the Paintings,
Drawings and Miniatures in the Barber
Institute of Fine Arts,* Cambridge:
University Press, 1952, pp. 132-133;
Pecírka no. 39

THE BARBER INSTITUTE OF FINE ARTS,
BIRMINGHAM UNIVERSITY, ENGLAND

Another form of theatrical entertainment
for Degas was the circus, those small,
permanent, indoor circuses characteristic of
Paris. In the Cirque Fernando, which was in
1898 to become the Cirque Medrano, he
made drawings of Mlle Lala whom Douglas
Cooper points out ("List of Emendations
to the Courtauld Catalogue," *Burlington,*
April 1954, p. 121) was a "negress or
mulatto who performed feats of strength."
This particular feat was hanging from a rope
by her teeth and being drawn upward to the
roof of the Cirque Fernando; this drawing,
which is dated January 25, 1879, seems
to have been the last in preparation for the
final painting. Although the figure of
Mlle Lala is superimposed with a grid of
lines to make transferral easy, the endurance
and effort of the acrobat are apparent in her
outthrust arms, the bending of her legs, even
the weight of her massive boots. Within the
figure of Mlle Lala there seem to be the
pressures of contours moving in different
directions, terminating in the softly
charcoaled mop of mulatto hair.

84 LE CIRQUE FERNANDO—*An Architectural
   Study* 1879
   VENTE IV: 255b VENTE stamp l.l.
   Study for LEMOISNE 522

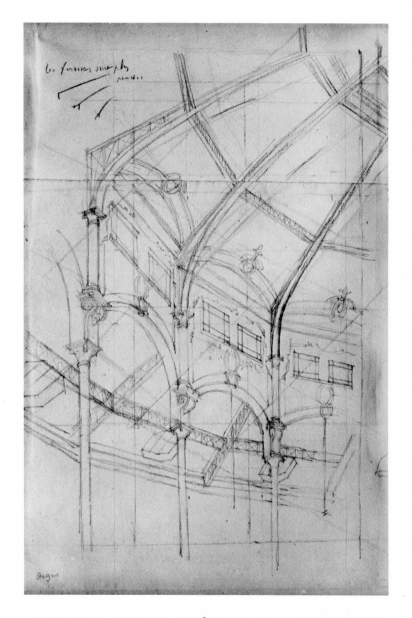

84

Black and red chalk on pink paper
19 x 12½ in. (48 x 31.3 cm.)
Inscription: "les fermes sont plus
penchées" u.l.
Related Studies: B.N. 23, pp. 30, 36-37,
45, 48
Provenance: Vente Atelier Degas IV, July
2-4, 1919, no. 255b; Dr. Georges Viau;
Jacques Seligmann & Co.; purchased 1938
Exhibitions: Cambridge 1931, no. 19b
*Literature: Handbook of the Barber Institute
of Fine Arts,* Birmingham, 1949, p. 19;
*Catalogue of the Paintings, Drawings and
Miniatures in the Barber Institute of Fine
Arts,* Cambridge: University Press, 1952,
pp. 134-135

THE BARBER INSTITUTE OF FINE ARTS,
BIRMINGHAM UNIVERSITY, ENGLAND

Degas was more interested in the settings
for the human figures than the drawings in
this exhibition might make it appear. He
analyzed the character of the rooms in
which the dancers rehearsed or suggested
the gas lamps and the trees of a café-concert.
Typical of this interest is the ceiling of the
Cirque Fernando which he not only studied
in this drawing but also in a series in a
notebook in the Bibliothèque Nationale in
Paris (BN pp. 30, 36-37, 45, 48), criticizing his
efforts, as he did here, by noting in the
upper left, "the roof beams bend more."
Although in the final version he only used
part of what we see here, it was important in
emphasizing the suspension in space of
Mlle Lala in the upper left corner of that
view of the Cirque Fernando.

85-87 *About 1879 Degas made some of his most
remarkable portraits of friends, and among
the wittiest are drawings and etchings of two
women, the American painter, Mary Cassatt,
and the French pantomime actress,
Ellen Andrée.*

*At the time that Degas drew the back of
Mary Cassatt (no. 85) and ruled lines over it
to make it easy to transfer for either the
pastel of her visiting the painting collection
at the Louvre (*LEMOISNE *581) or the etching
in the Etruscan galleries (*DELTEIL *30), he and
she were collaborating closely in the hope of
being able to produce a periodical devoted to
print-making which they intended to call* Le

85

Jour et la Nuit. *In this drawing Degas did not show Miss Cassatt's face but seemed instead to illustrate a point a friend, Edmond Duranty, had made in his* La Nouvelle Peinture *of 1876, "With a back we can discover a temperament, an age, a social position." Miss Cassatt, independent, well-bred, self-assured and about thirty-five, leans part of her weight back upon her umbrella as she looks at works of art at the Louvre.*

Following Miss Cassatt discreetly from behind a catalogue is a seated woman whom Degas modified in the compositional drawing so that she would share our complete absorption in Miss Cassatt. In the independent drawing of her (no. 86) Degas had her sit back with more reserve and he used white chalk to enliven the cuffs of her dress and to draw our attention to the precise and somewhat supercilious features of her face. She seems the essence of gentility which makes Frederick Sweet's suggestion that she is Miss Cassatt's sister Lyda most convincing (Frederick A. Sweet, Miss Mary Cassatt, *Norman: University of Oklahoma Press, 1966).*

*Finally Degas made another study in the Louvre (no. 87) which has been identified with Miss Cassatt and which is related to a pastel of approximately the same size (*LEMOISNE 532*) which Degas inscribed, "Portraits en frise pour décoration dans un appartement." The pose of this stocky woman at the left seems uninhibited, and even brazen, compared with the American painter. Even in the drawing of her at the right there is none of the self-conscious refinement of gesture which Miss Cassatt's companion reveals as she also holds a book. The difference in "temperament and social position," if not in age, suggests that this is Ellen Andrée who wore a similar hat and dress in a small etching (*DELTEIL 20*) Degas made of her about this same time. Degas probably had her assume a role which would be the reverse of Miss Cassatt's.*

85 MARY CASSATT AT THE LOUVRE C. 1879
VENTE IV: 250b VENTE stamp l.l.
ATELIER stamp u.r.
Study for LEMOISNE 581 and DELTEIL 30
Pencil

86

11¾ x 9½ in. (30 x 24 cm.) (sight)
Related Studies: VENTE IV: 249b
Provenance: Vente Atelier Degas IV, July
2-4, 1919, no. 250b; Guérin; private
collection, France
Exhibitions: Paris 1955, no. 76
Literature: Boggs p. 51 (not illustrated); Paul
Moses, *An Exhibition of Etchings by Edgar
Degas*, The Renaissance Society, The
University of Chicago, 1964, no. 30
(not illustrated)

THE JOAN AND LESTER AVNET COLLECTION,
NEW YORK

86 WOMAN READING A CATALOGUE C. 1879

VENTE III: 150(2)   VENTE stamp l.l.
Study for LEMOISNE 581
Charcoal and pastel on gray paper
white
19 x 12¼ in. (48 x 31 cm.)
Provenance: Vente Atelier Degas III, April
7-9, 1919, no. 150; Sale, Various Properties,
Sotheby's, July 1, 1964, no. 62; Frank Perls

MR. AND MRS. HAROLD MIRISCH, BEVERLY HILLS

87 *Two Studies of* MARY CASSATT *or*
ELLEN ANDREE *in the Louvre* by 1879

Charcoal and pastel on gray paper
18¾ x 24¾ in. (27.8 x 63 cm.)
Inscription: "Degas" u.r.
Related Work: LEMOISNE 532
Provenance: Harris Whittemore (*Sale
Collection of Late Harris Whittemore,*
Parke-Barnet, New York, March, 1948,
no. 84)
Exhibitions: Boston 1935, no. 125; Boston,
Museum of Fine Arts, 1939, *Loan Exhibition
of Paintings and Drawings from New
England Collections,* no. 158; Washington,
National Gallery of Art, 1944-45;
Washington 1947, no. 17; New York,
Columbia University at Knoedler, 1959
(October 13-November 7), *Great Master
Drawings of Seven Centuries,* no. 72

MRS. SIEGFRIED KRAMARSKY, NEW YORK

88-89 *The Florentine, Diego Martelli, probably met
Degas in 1858-59 when the French painter
was living in Florence and would
occasionally go to the Café Michelangiolo
where young Italian artists, who were to be
known later as the Macchiaioli, gathered.*

87

Martelli was himself a writer, a critic and, above all, a propagandist for this group of artists. When he went to Paris in 1862 and 1868 he may have renewed his acquaintance with Degas, but when he returned in 1878 he found himself "running the risk of becoming a friend of Degas" as he wrote some friends, on December 25 of that year. Martelli and Degas were both part of an Italian colony in Paris in which Giuseppe de Nittis, Boldini, Signorini (as a visitor) and Zandomeneghi were particular friends.

Degas dated the drawing of Martelli (no. 88), one week before the opening of the fourth Impressionist exhibition. Martelli, as a propagandist, appreciated what an enthusiastic one Degas was in promoting this exhibition of Independent artists. Martelli went to the opening on April 10th and took pleasure in seeing two portraits of himself, one (LEMOISNE 519) by Degas, the other by Zandomeneghi (presumably the one of that date now in the Galleria d'Arte Moderna in Florence). Impressed by that exhibition Martelli, on his return to Italy in 1879, gave a lecture to the Circolo filologico at Leghorn called Gli Impressionisti; it was printed the next year, the first study of Impressionism in Italian.

The Drey drawing (no. 88) is, like VENTE III: 344 in the Fogg Art Museum, a full study of the figure of Martelli for the painting in Edinburgh (LEMOISNE 519); Martelli's waistcoat is of the same cut. Both are squared for transferral but the Drey drawing, which is more developed and gives more information about the setting, is closer to the final result. Since its date is so close to the opening of the exhibition in which it was shown—one week before—it is possible that the Fogg drawing is the working study and this a record of the painting—perhaps intended for Martelli himself. It is a forceful drawing in which the brusque strokes of the pencil indicate the weight of Martelli's body, the pressure of his arms crossed in front of his generous stomach, and the delicate balancing of that mass on the fragile scissor chair.

The expression on Martelli's face in the Drey drawing is more thoughtful and serious than in the finished version of the painting. On the other hand, if the

88

89

Cleveland head (no. 89) doesn't have quite the painting's ebullience, the twisted mouth and lifted eyebrow do give it the suggestion of a face whose expression easily could be transformed completely. It is closer, like the second Fogg drawing (VENTE III: 344 (1)), to the freer and horizontal version of the painting (LEMOISNE 520) which is now in Buenos Aires. Degas had used the combination of white chalk and black charcoal on brown paper to give it a mellow luminosity.

88 PORTRAIT OF DIEGO MARTELLI April 3, 1879

VENTE I: 326
Study for LEMOISNE 519
Black chalk, heightened with white
17¾ x 11½ in. (45 x 29 cm.)
Inscription: "chez Martelli / 3 avril 79 / Degas" u.l.
Provenance: Vente Atelier Degas I, May 6-8, 1918, no. 326; Fevre (*Vente Jeanne Fevre*, Charpentier, Paris, June 12, 1934, no. 23); Duveen; Sir Kenneth Clark, London; Mr. and Mrs. F. A. Drey, London
Related Literature: Letters of Martelli to Matilde and G. Gioli, *Lettere Martelli*, 158bis nos. 12-25b, Biblioteca Marucelliana, Florence; Boggs p. 123; Lamberto Vitali, "Three Italian Friends of Degas," *Burlington*, June 1963, pp. 269-270

MR. AND MRS. R. E. A. DREY, BEXLEYHEATH, KENT

89 PORTRAIT OF DIEGO MARTELLI 1879

VENTE III: 160 (1) VENTE stamp l.l.
Study for LEMOISNE 520
Charcoal and white chalk on brown paper
17⅜ x 12⅜ in. (44 x 31.3 cm.)
Provenance: Vente Atelier Degas III, April 7-9, 1919, no. 160 (1); Dr. Georges Viau; Demotte; B. Natanson; acquired by Cleveland Museum of Art 1953
Literature: Rivière no. 91; H. Francis, *The Bulletin of the Cleveland Museum of Art*, XLIV, December 1957, cover and p. 216; Pecírka no. 40; Moskowitz and Mongan No. 786

THE CLEVELAND MUSEUM OF ART 53.268
John L. Severance Fund

90 SABINE NEYT 1877-80

VENTE IV: 272a VENTE stamp l.l.

90

91

Study for LEMOISNE 430
Charcoal on gray paper
18¾ x 11¾ in. (47.5 x 30 cm.)
Related Works: LEMOISNE 497, 576; VENTE IV:
252
Provenance: Vente Atelier Degas IV, July
2-4, 1919, no. 272a; Mr. and Mrs.
Frederick Stafford
Exhibitions: New Orleans 1965, p. 93, pl.
XXIX
ISAAC DELGADO MUSEUM OF ART, NEW ORLEANS
Gift of Mr. and Mrs. Frederick Stafford 1964
One of the models who posed as a
seamstress or chaperone for Degas's ballet
compositions was his maid, Sabine Neyt.
By inscribing one drawing (VENTE IV: 252)
he made it possible to identify the rest:
"Ma vieille bonne Sabine Neyt, morte à
Paris, 21, rue Pigalle." One of her roles in
his paintings was to help the young dancers
adjust their *tutus.* In this drawing she is
respectably bonneted and shawled, the
roughness of the charcoal describing her
lack of pretension, her homely face smiling
gently as she concentrated upon her task.
At the same time there is a classical
containment and dignity in her total form
which makes the drawing something more
than descriptive and anecdotal.

91 MELINA DARDE SEATED December 1878

VENTE II: 230 (1) VENTE stamp l.l.
Pencil
12¼ x 9 in. (31 x 23 cm.)
Inscription: "pâle, vert, marbré / mains
bisées / corsage bas comme une cuirasse /
en piqué blanc," u.l.; "cheveux châtains
clairs / tout le tour de la tête est couvert
d'une poussière de petits cheveux excepté
le devant," u.r.; "Melina Darde / 15 ans /
danseuse à la Gaîté / Dec. 78." l.l.
Related Works: VENTE III: 133 (3)
Provenance: Vente Atelier Degas II,
December 11-13, 1918, no. 230 (1);
Paul Mathey
Exhibitions: Paris 1924, no. 126; Paris 1937,
no. 95; Galerie André Weil, 1939 (June 9-30),
Degas, Peintre des Nouvement, no. 23
Literature: La Vie Moderne, Thursday, May
8, 1879, p. 71 (as no. 2, Exposition des
Indépendants); Rivière pl. 33; Browse no.
68; Leymarie no. 16; Pecírka no. 38; Roger-
Marx no. 1
BARONESS ALAIN DE GUNZBURG, PARIS

One of the dancers whom Sabine Neyt might have tended was Melina Darde who, Degas tells us in an inscription on this drawing, was 15 years old and a dancer at the *théâtre de la Gaité* in December, 1878. Degas became interested in the young dancers at this time—the frailty of their thin arms, their weariness, and yet their self-discipline which we can see in Melina Darde's exercising the points of her shoes. We discover from his notes on the drawing just how observant he was about costume and how conscious of such youthful details as the dusting of small hairs over the head of Melina Darde. Although his pencil works incisively, accenting for example the curve of her left foot, and moves as rhythmically as a dance itself swelling out from Melina's arms into the bow of her legs, he also makes her infinitely touching, particularly since we look down at her, small and helpless below. Another drawing inscribed with her name (VENTE III: 359 (1)) is clearly a study for the *Rehearsal* in the Frick Museum (LEMOISNE 537) for which no. 96 is a study.

92 TWO YOUNG DANCERS AT REST C. 1878

LEMOISNE 480
Study for LEMOISNE 479
Pastel on browned paper
24 x 22 in. (61 x 56 cm.)
Inscription: "Degas" l.l.
Provenance: Henri Lerolle; Hector Brame
Exhibitions: Paris 1937, no. 91; Amsterdam, Stedelijk Museum, 1938, *Fransche Kunst,* no. 101; Amsterdam 1946, no. 76; Bern 1951-52, no. 25; Winterthur 1957, *Europaische Meister,* no. 232; Paris 1959, (March-May) *De Géricault à Matisse, Chefs-d'Oeuvres Français des Collections Suisses,* no. 154; Wolfburg 1961, *Französische Malerei von Delacroix bis Picasso,* no. 40; Lausanne, 1964, *Chefs d'Oeuvres Français des Collections Suisse de Manet à Picasso,* no. 7
Literature: Lafond vol. II, cover; Rivière no. 94; Lemoisne no. 480; Cooper no. 12; "La Danse," *Du,* May 1950
MRS. MARIANNE FEILCHENFELDT, ZURICH

In the oil painting, for which this pastel is a study, these two young dancers are foils for the strongly characterized ballet master and slumping chaperone. Here, however,

93

Degas permitted them to be completely
endearing. We see more of the dancer at the
left, whose long hair, luminous skirt and
dutifully pointed toe are enchanting; even
the other dancer reveals an adolescent
femininity as she touches her ear. Placing
these figures toward the right of the page,
with its edge bisecting the dancer at the
right, cannot be explained as the
consequence of Degas's eccentricity or
obsession with accidental effects; the
dancers are so firmly rooted back into space
and so harmoniously related to each other
that the effect is one of classical satisfaction.
At the same time the asymmetry makes us
tenderly conscious of their vulnerability
and youth.

93 DANCER WITH A FAN C. 1879

LEMOISNE 545
Pastel
17¾ x 11⅜ in. (45 x 29 cm.)
Inscription: "Degas" u.l.
Related Drawing: BROWSE 128
Provenance: Henri Rouart (Vente, Galerie
Manzi-Joyant, December 16, 1912, no. 75);
Mme Ernest Rouart
Exhibitions: Paris 1924, no. 122; Paris,
Galerie Charpentier, 1928 (June 1-30), *La
Jeunesse,* no. 96; Paris: Seligmann, 1933,
Pastel français, no. 69; Paris 1937, no. 97;
Paris 1955, no. 84; Paris 1960, no. 25
Literature: G. W. Thornley, *Quinze
lithographies d'après Degas,* Paris: Boussod,
Valadon & Cie, n.d. (c. 1889); A. Alexandre,
Les Arts, December 1912; Coquiot, *Degas,*
p. 72; Grappe; Denis Rouart, *Degas à la
recherche de sa technique,* Paris: Floury,
1945, pp. 22, 24, 25; Lemoisne 545; Roger-
Marx, no. 4

PRIVATE COLLECTION, COURTESY OF THE
DALLAS MUSEUM OF FINE ARTS

Degas was conscious of a premature
adulthood in some of the young dancers.
This ballerina has the body of a child but
the exaggerated features and the dignity of
an adult as we look down upon her standing
against the vast, empty floor of the rehearsal
room. It is a work in which any sympathy
expressed in the thin arms and bony chest
and any humor conveyed in the strong
profile and rearing skirt are subordinated to
the gently poetic atmosphere of silvery light

95

94

within the room. Denis Rouart has described the process as one in which Degas began with a conventional pastel drawing onto which he blew steam from boiling water until it produced a paste into which he could work with a stiff brush; this made it possible to produce a gentle atmospheric effect in certain areas; whereas others, for example the dancer herself, were left to emerge from the film as he had originally drawn them with the strokes of his pastel.

94-95 *Sometime late in the spring of 1879 Degas wrote to his friend Bracquemond (LETTRES p. 44) about the fourth Impressionist exhibition: "There is a room of fans, believe it or not." We know that he had submitted five and that Pissarro had contributed nine; and it is possible that there were others, all a tribute to the influence of Japanese art. To Degas the shape of the fan itself must have suggested the panoramic scope of the operatic stage for he used it for large compositions of dancers who seem minute against the vastness of the floors and flats. In contrast to the scale of the scene, his handling of the small surfaces of the fans was miniature-like. He used gouache loosely and thinly on the background but became more precise in describing the figures in the foreground. He even added discreet touches of silver and gold to add to their enchantment.*

Since, in the fan in the Lindberg collection (no. 94), our view is interrupted by the flats, we must be high above the stage itself, looking down at the dancers, who are performing for an audience to the right of the fan, and into the wings, where a group of top-hatted admirers stands. The effect, which Degas achieved with a combination of media, is one of wonderment—at our own rarified position and at touches of exquisite beauty of the kind we find in the description of the dancers' disciplined legs.

The Schmidheiny fan (no. 95) reveals how much less inhibited Degas was in the suggestion of movement in his fans than he was in his more formal paintings at the same time. The fan is a delight, partly because of the mocking humor with which Degas drew the elderly première danseuse *dropping into a curtsy and the sprightly movement of the very young dancer in the center, but also*

96

*because there is a tenderness in his
description of the wavering corps de ballet.
We cannot help but be pleased by the
continuity, varied by changes in tempo, as
our eyes are led through the pattern of the
dancers' limbs.*

94 FAN WITH DANCERS C. 1879

LEMOISNE 564
Essence, gouache, pastel, silver and gold
7 x 23½ in. (18 x 60 cm.)
Inscription: "Degas" l.l.
Provenance: Durand-Ruel
Literature: Lemoisne no. 564; Bouret p. 128

MR. AND MRS. W. HILDING LINDBERG,
TACOMA, WASHINGTON

95 FAN WITH LA FARANDOLE 1879

LEMOISNE 557
Gouache on silk, mounted on cardboard,
with some silver and gold
12 x 14 in. (30.7 x 61 cm.), Fan-shaped
Inscription: "Degas" u.l.
Provenance: Durand-Ruel; Vente Succession
Mme X . . ., Hotel Drouot, Paris, February 13,
1918, no. 77; G. Pellet; M. Exsteens
Exhibitions: Paris 1937, no. 186; London,
the Leicester Galleries, 1938, *The Dance,*
no. 30; Paris, Galerie André Weil, 1939
(June 9-30), *Degas, peintre du mouvement,*
no. 20; Paris, Galerie Charpentier, 1948-49,
Danse et Divertissements, no. 75; Bern
1951-52, no. 30; Amsterdam 1952, no. 23;
Paris 1955, no. 86; Bern, Klipstein und
Kornfeld, 1960 (October 22-November 30),
Choix d'une collection privée, no. 15;
Bregenz, 1965, Meisterwerke am Bodensee,
no. 30b, pl. 10
Literature: Lafond II, p. 34; Georges Rivière,
Monsieur Degas, Paris: Floury, 1938, p. 157;
Daniel Wildenstein, "Degas", *Les Arts,*
June 8, 1955, No. 518

MAX SCHMIDHEINY, HEERBRUGG, SWITZERLAND

96-98 *One of the important figures in dancing
classes and rehearsals was the violinist. In
the past he had conducted the classes while
he played. Degas's most appealing violinist
was probably the bulky, bearded figure
(no. 96) whom he studied for the Rehearsal
in the Frick Collection. The charcoal
drawing, which has the substantial quality*

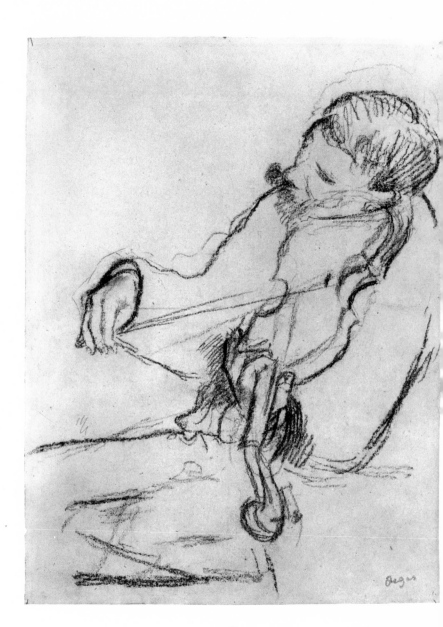

97

98

*of the drawings of Diego Martelli (see nos.
88 and 89), also shows the animation with
which Degas hunted the right position for
the violin. Peter Wick has argued that, in
working toward the more sentimental figure
in the finished painting, Degas had fused
this earthy Jewish violinist with the younger
man who sat for drawings nos. 97 and 98.*

*Degas did not leave the studies of this young
violinist alone. In the two best known
versions, a pastel and charcoal drawing in
the Metropolitan (LEMOISNE 451) and a
Dancing Lesson with a single dancer at the
bar in the Havemeyer Collection (LEMOISNE
459), Degas used the same position as in
drawings nos. 97 and 98, but he creased a
frown in the forehead, sunk a hollow in the
cheek and made a central part in the
musician's thinning hair. The vigorous
charcoal drawing (no. 97) is probably a
study for all versions; in it there is only a
hint of the romantic in the bent head. The
pastel (no. 98) is closer to the charcoal and
seems an effort to neutralize the personality
of the violinist in an overall nostalgic effect.
Degas probably preferred that his musicians
provide passive accompaniments in every
sense to the activities of the dance.*

96   THE VIOLINIST   C. 1879

VENTE III: 161 (a)   VENTE stamp l.l.
Study for LEMOISNE 537
Charcoal with white on blue-gray paper
16½ x 11¾ in. (42 x 30 cm.)
Related Works: VENTE III: 161 (b)
Provenance: Vente Atelier Degas III, April
7-9, 1919, no. 161 (a); Marcel Guérin
collection, Paris
Exhibitions: New York 1958, no. 23, p. XIX;
New York 1960, no. 93
Literature: Rouart 1948, no. 3; Peter A. Wick,
"Degas's Violinist," *Bulletin, Museum of
Fine Arts, Boston,* vol. LVII, no. 310, 1959,
cover and pp. 87-101; Huttinger p. 42;
Clark, vol. I, p. 83, fig. 66

MUSEUM OF FINE ARTS, BOSTON 58.1263
William Francis Warden Fund

97   THE VIOLINIST   1880

VENTE IV: 247b   VENTE stamp l.r.
Study for LEMOISNE 450, 451
Pencil
12⅝ x 9½ in. (32 x 24 cm.)

99

Provenance: Vente Atelier Degas IV, July
2-4, 1919, no. 247b; Vignier; A. E. Gallatin;
Guy Stein; Durand-Ruel; Chester Beatty;
Charles E. Slatkin
Exhibitions: New York, Metropolitan
Museum of Art, 1924, *The Gallatin
Collection,* no. 85; London, Reid Gallery,
1961 (spring), *French Masters of the 19th
and 20th Centuries,* no. 7. Minneapolis and
New York 1962, no. 28
Literature: Peter Wick, "Degas' Violinist,"
Bulletin, Museum of Fine Arts Boston, vol.
LVII, no. 310, 1959, p. 97 (not illustrated)
PRIVATE COLLECTION

98 THE VIOLINIST 1880

Pastel
23⅜ x 20 in. (60 x 51 cm.)
Inscription: "Degas / 80" l.l.
Provenance: Paul Cassirer, Amsterdam
Exhibitions: Amsterdam 1938, no. 103
PRIVATE COLLECTION, SWITZERLAND

99 TWO STUDIES OF A DANCER 1879-1880

VENTE III: 277   VENTE stamp l.l.
Study for the wax sculpture of 1880,
Petite Danseuse de quatorze ans
Chalk and pastel on gray paper
18 x 22½ in. (46 x 57 cm.)
Related Studies: See Lemoisne 586bis, ter;
VENTE III: 341 (2); 386; VENTE IV: 287a
Provenance: Vente Atelier Degas III, April
7-9, 1919, no. 277; Cottevielle; sold
Sotheby's, London, July 4, 1962, no. 35
MAX RAYNE, LONDON

What little documentation there is about
the sculpture of Degas comes from a work
he intended to exhibit in the fifth
Impressionist exhibition in 1880 but, since
it was not finished, did not appear until the
next year; he described it in both catalogues
as a small dancer fourteen years old. When
he did show the work he dressed the tinted
wax body with a white linen bodice, a white
gauze *tutu,* tied a blue silk ribbon around
her hair and gave her real ballet shoes. He
had made a great many studies for this work
including another sculpture of her nude.
The exhibition's drawing could easily be
early since he later abandoned the longer
skirts for a short *tutu* which would show the
thighs and knees of the small dancer. Degas

100

was charmed especially by the effort with which the ballerina clasped her hands behind her back while assuming the traditional fourth position of the dance, and he maintained this pose in all the studies. The weight of the charcoal seems a form of exploration, changing its pressures as it describes the strains of those picturesque arms. The link between the sculpture and the drawing exists, certainly in the two slightly different angles from which the figure is observed, but also in this feeling that the weight and movement of the line on a flat sheet of paper can give a sense of the discovery of forms in space.

100 YOUNG BALLERINA RESTING C. 1880-82

VENTE III: 109 (3) VENTE stamp l.l.
ATELIER stamp *verso*
Charcoal on heavy cream paper
$9^{13}/_{16}$ x 11½ in. (24.8 x 29.5 cm.)
Inscription: "repos se caressant les genoux," u.r.
Related Drawings: BROWSE 76, 77, 78
Provenance: Vente Atelier Degas III, April 7-9, 1919, no. 109 (3); Bernheim-Jeune; gift of Julius Boehler 1926

THE MINNEAPOLIS INSTITUTE OF ARTS
Gift of Julius Boehler 1926

Although homelier and, at rest, cockier than another little ballet *rat* Degas drew practising at the bar at the same time, this small dancer can be recognized from the words Miss Browse (BROWSE p. 364, no. 76) uses for the other, "all Degas's drawing of her show the faults which might be expected of a beginner, especially the *knobly* knees whose muscles she has not yet learned to draw up, and the *drooping* elbows." Degas described her in his inscription on the drawing as rubbing those knobby knees as she rests. At the same time every crisp pencil line reveals the cocky gamin, the worldly Montmartre soul that dominates the body of the child.

101 A CORYPHEE RESTING C. 1880-82

LEMOISNE 659
Pastel on gray paper
18⅞ x 24½ in. (45 x 59 cm.)
Inscription: "Degas" u.r.
Provenance: Van Wisselingh Collection
Exhibitions: Washington 1947, no. 2

101

Literature: International Studio, vol. 76, p. 8; Lemoisne 659; Browse no. 49; Janson, *Bulletin des Musées Royaux des Beaux-Arts*, Brussels, no. 2, June 1956, p. 80, figure 5
JOHN G. JOHNSON COLLECTION, PHILADELPHIA

The conception for this pastel could have grown out of the piquant ballet *rat* in no. 100, but Degas used several devices to romanticize her slightly. First of all he made her a little older so that her legs are stronger, her elbows softer and her head smaller in relation to her body. He has used the ribbon around her throat and the bracelet around her wrist to make her more feminine; he has even spread out her *tutu*. His pastel, both in its color and texture, is gentler than his pencil. Finally, although there is something of the tom-boy still in her position, he has made her dreamily reflective, as if a feminine self-consciousness was coming into being. The traditional title for this work of a Coryphée or ballet company star may be a gentle form of compliment or more probably a gentle form of irony.

102-104　*Sometime about 1882 Degas must have made his last drawings of jockeys at the racetracks. These jockeys share youth and a cocky self-assurance in common with the ballet rats Degas was painting at the same time. They are perhaps a little older and certainly more skillful so that they succeed in seeming more convincingly debonnaire. They are also brashly male which Degas emphasized with the brusque, angular strokes of his pencil or stick of charcoal or pastel. But under their large caps and colorful silks they share with the small ballerinas the spirit of the street urchin.*

All of these have the immediacy of drawings made on the spot. Substantial changes and marginal studies are apparent in the large charcoal drawing of a jockey in action on his horse (no. 102) but they do not detract from the bold impression of the figure and the concentration on his homely face. The three studies of a jockey in no. 103 are in the intense blue pencil Degas sometimes used in a notebook in the early eighties (BN 5); here he applied it particularly gently to the central figure and to the repetition of his reflective face at the right. The third jockey (no. 104) leans back on his horse with

102

103

marvelous, if ungainly bravado, his spirit
echoed in the quick and daring strokes of
Degas's charcoal and pastel. Such drawings
seem to have become part of the painter's
stock to be used in varying combinations in
his paintings or more developed pastels.

102 JOCKEY IN PROFILE C. 1882

VENTE III: 98(2) VENTE Stamp l.l.
Used as Study for LEMOISNE 850 or 889
Charcoal on cream paper
18⅞ x 12¼ in. (48 x 31 cm.)
Related Drawings: VENTE IV: 373; 384a;
III: 351 (2); 131 (1); 351 (1)
Provenance: Vente Atelier Degas III, April
7-9, 1919, no. 98 (2); P. M. Turner
Literature: Bouret p. 244

JOHN BRYSON, OXFORD

103 JOCKEYS *(Three Studies)* 1882-84

VENTE III: 104 (2) VENTE stamp l.r.
Study for LEMOISNE 755
Blue pencil
9 x 11¾ in. (23 x 30 cm.)
Provenance: Vente Atelier Degas III, April
7-9, 1919, no. 104(2); bought by Marcel
Guérin; Vente Marcel Guérin, Hotel Drouot,
Paris, December 12, 1936, no. 1bis; bought
by Durand-Ruel; bought by present owner
from Durand-Ruel February 12, 1939
Exhibitions: Bern 1951-52, no. 125;
Amsterdam 1952, no. 65; Paris 1960, no. 6

BARON LOUIS DE CHOLLET, FRIBOURG

104 MOUNTED JOCKEY 1882-84

VENTE III: 107 (3) VENTE stamp l.l.
Charcoal heightened with pastel
11¾ x 9 in. (30 x 23 cm.)
Related Work: LEMOISNE 702, painted
before 1884
Provenance: Vente Atelier Degas III, April
7-9, 1919, no. 107 (3); bought by Durand-
Ruel; sold to Percy Moore Turner June 29,
1929; bought by present owner from
Durand-Ruel 1950
Exhibitions: Bern 1951-52, no. 127
Literature: Bouret p. 244

BARON LOUIS DE CHOLLET, FRIBOURG

105-107 *In the second half of the 1880's, Degas's*
studies of horses and riders were based on

104

*memory and the revision of earlier drawings,
or upon two somewhat contradictory media
—sculpture and photography. For example
the drawing of a jockey which is no. 105
is close to a jockey in the pastel* LEMOISNE
*number 755 but, with the application of
pastel to the pencil, it is softer and more
diffuse; even the description of the jockey
does not have the same animation as in the
earlier work. The colors in the pastel play
upon an element of passive melancholy, a
quality with which Degas would struggle
intermittently the rest of his life.*

*The struggle is apparent in the powerful
drawing of the nude jockey (no. 106). Here
Degas not only worked from memory but
tried to recapture the twisting movement of
the rider in space; the strong charcoal
models the figure as rhythmically as if it
were taking form under his hands out of
clay. Although the dating of Degas's
sculptures is by no means fixed most of the
wax horses would seem to fit into the 1880's,
and the enjoyment Degas received in
modeling these horses is echoed in the
contours here.*

*On the other hand there was also that flat,
illusionistic record that photography
produced and which from the first
captivated Degas. In the 1880's Degas had a
keen interest in the photographs of animals
and men in motion by the American
photographer E. J. Muybridge; these were
first reproduced in Paris in* Le Globe *on
September 27, 1881. Aaron Sharf shows (see
below) that drawing no. 107 in the
exhibition was based on the photographs
Muybridge took of a horse called Annie G.
in 1883-85 which were published in* Animal
Location *until 1887. These stimulated Degas
to consider the effects of action once more,
and he made some drawings and sculpture
from Muybridge's works. Sharf pointed out
(p. 192) that, "Degas seems to have
preferred . . . those positions in which a more
subtle implication of movement was
suggested and which, in the light of pictorial
convention, appeared the least natural."
Although these drawings would seem to be
a contradiction of sculpture in their very
suggestion of speed, Degas began to make
impressions (the reverse of this is* VENTE IV:
335b*), which may have been an effort to see
the same figure as one could in sculpture*

105

from two diametrically different points of view. Whereas this had been a rare device at the time he drew the horse in no. 60, it was now his normal practice.

105 JOCKEY 1885-90

VENTE IV: 231b VENTE stamp l.l.
Study after LEMOISNE 755
Pencil with pastel
12⅝ x 9½ in. (32 x 24 cm.)
Provenance: Vente Atelier Degas IV, July 2-4, 1919, no. 231b; Vignier; Albert E. Gallatin; Durand-Ruel 1948; bought by present owner 1955
Exhibitions: Paris 1960, no. 5; Lausanne 1964, *Chefs d'Oeuvre des Collections Suisses,* no. 10

BARON LOUIS DE CHOLLET, FRIBOURG

106 STUDY FOR A JOCKEY C. 1887-90

VENTE III: 131(2) VENTE stamp l.r.
ATELIER stamp *verso*
Charcoal
12¼ x 9¾ in. (31 x 24.9 cm.)
Provenance: Vente Atelier Degas III, April 7-9, 1919, no. 131 (2); Dr. Georges Viau; F. Koenigs; gift of D. G. van Beuningen 1940
Exhibitions: Amsterdam 1946, no. 62
Literature: Longstreet

MUSEUM BOYMANS-VAN BEUNINGEN, ROTTERDAM F 11.129

107 HORSE AND JOCKEY 1887-90

ATELIER stamp *verso*
VENTE III: 130 (1) VENTE stamp l.l.
Red chalk on white paper
11⅛ x 16⅜ in. (28.3 x 41.8 cm.)
Provenance: Vente Atelier Degas III, April 7-9, 1919, no. 130 (1); Vente M. X... (Fevre), Hotel Drouot, June 22, 1925, no. 41, ill. p. 15; M. Hain; F. Koenigs
Exhibitions: Amsterdam 1946, no. 56; Paris-Brussels-Amsterdam-Rotterdam, 1949-50, *Le dessin français de Fouquet à Cézanne,* no. 198; Bern 1951/52, no. 98; Paris, Bibliothèque Nationale, 1952 (February 20-April 20), *Dessins du XVᵉ au XIXᵉ siècle Musée Boymans de Rotterdam,* no. 135
Literature: Huyghe & Jaccottet, pl. 96; Hüttinger p. 68; Rosenberg no. 217; Longstreet; Aaron Scharf, "Painting, Photography and the Image of Movement,"

106

107

Burlington, May 1962, p. 191 and p. 195
(repr. fig. 13)

108 *Sketch for* PAGANS AND DEGAS'S FATHER 1882

VENTE II: 125   VENTE stamp l.l.
LEMOISNE 346
Study for LEMOISNE 345
Pastel
18⅞ x 24¼ in. (53 x 62 cm.)
Provenance: Vente Atelier Degas II,
December 11-13, 1918, no. 125; Fevre
collection, Monte Carlo; Durand-Ruel;
Carroll S. Tyson, Philadelphia
Exhibitions: Philadelphia, Philadelphia
Museum of Art, 1947, *Masterpieces of
Philadelphia Collections,* no. 127
Literature: Lemoisne 346; "Tyson
Collection," *Philadelphia Museum of Art
Bulletin,* Winter 1964, p. 78
Related Literature: Giuseppe de Nittis,
Notes et Souvenirs, Paris: Reuniés, 1895,
p. 220; Mme Alphonse Daudet, *Souvenirs
autour d'un groupe littéraire,* Paris:
Charpentier, 1910, p. 98; Lettres p. 68
PHILADELPHIA MUSEUM OF ART
Mr. and Mrs. Carroll S. Tyson Collection
Shown only at Philadelphia Museum of Art

One of the most welcome guests at the
evening parties Degas occasionally attended
was the Spanish guitarist and tenor, Lorenzo
Pagans. He had been introduced to Paris in
Semiramis at the Opera in 1860 (see no. 37).
The writer Edmond de Goncourt said of him,
"He is our musician." Degas's father must
have felt the same way because Degas had
painted two portraits of him with Pagans
about 1872 (LEMOISNE 256, 257) and, when
he worked on another portrait of the
musician almost a decade after his father's
death, he permitted Auguste de Gas to
intrude into the background in this
preparatory drawing only as a faint smudge.
Pagans had aged over the years but he still
possessed, as the wife of Alphonse Daudet
wrote, "the same face, the same allure, the
same voice—always thirty-five." Although
Degas's drawings were seldom
compositional, it is possible that he had
conceived his portrait of Pagans originally
as he drew it here in charcoal and pastel.
The deliberate pushing of the figure to one

108

side, while giving the musician a character
assertive enough to dominate the total space,
was typical of his portraiture at this time.
The form and shape of the drawing rise out
of the rough strokes of charcoal; the color
of the pastel was added later to provide
compositional emphasis and to give the
suggestion of an atmospheric warmth with
which Degas must have identified Pagans.

109 MME DIETZ-MONIN 1880-85

VENTE I: 199 VENTE stamp l.l.
LEMOISNE 619
Pastel on cardboard
20 x 20 in. (51 x 51 cm.)
Provenance: Vente Atelier Degas I, May 6-8,
1918, no. 199; Sommer; Durand-Ruel
Exhibitions: New York, Paul Rosenberg &
Co., 1955-56 (December 19-January 14)
19th and 20th Century French Paintings,
no. 8
Literature: Lemoisne 619

MR. AND MRS. GUSTAVE RING, WASHINGTON, D.C.

Lemoisne suggests that this is Mme Dietz-
Monin but, if it is, she appears younger than
she did in 1879 when Degas first painted her
(LEMOISNE 534-536); her nose is straighter
and her mouth more generous. If it is Mme
Dietz-Monin, that generosity would have
been necessary to have forgiven the letter
Degas angrily wrote her (LETTRES p. 56)
when she had posed for the earlier painting.
On the other hand she resembles another
unknown woman Degas drew twice later
(LEMOISNE 797, 798). Whoever she is, her
face is amused and radiant and her gesture
has an openness which Degas, a connoisseur
of gestures, must have loved.

110-112 *Degas restlessly explored various themes in*
the 1880's. One grew out of his visits to
millinery shops with the painter Mary
Cassatt or with Mme Straus, the widow of
the composer Bizet. Although he himself
said he was attracted to this subject by the
red fingers of the girl who handled the pins
(LEMOISNE vol. I, p. 123), it is clear that he
was affected by the flower-like hats
themselves and by the perspective of a
millinery shop where he could look down at
the hats and the seated customers. He dated
three developed pastels of such
establishments 1882 (LEMOISNE 681-683),

109

and these three pastel drawings (nos. 110 to 112) are in different ways related to them.

Miss Cassatt told her friend Mrs. Havemeyer that she would pose for Degas's millinery pictures when the need arose. Obviously this large drawing (no. 110) was such a case, for Miss Cassatt's face is shadowed and indistinct and she herself is only identifiable by the small black dog she clutches. Nevertheless, as Degas protectively places her under us and against the dark chair, she seems the essence of gentility— the kind of customer who would buy the handsome, ribboned, feathered hat she wears. The second pastel drawing (no. 111) is of a stalwart and comic figure—the saleswoman determined to snub her customers. Her expressively caricatured profile and twisted arms do not completely surmount the sobriety of her navy blue dress and shadowed environment. Finally (no. 112), in a different air and sun-filled world, three customers, wearing their pretty bonnets, lean on a rail fence and chat. Their bodies have the jauntiness of Degas's studies of jockeys at the same time—but their absorption in each other's words and their dress is completely feminine. All three point out Degas's tendency at this time to draw in pastel over charcoal, exploiting their softness of texture and colour but also producing a certain somberness from the emergence of the black.

110 WOMAN SEATED *(after Miss Cassatt)* 1882-84

LEMOISNE 796bis
Pastel
28 x 19 in. (71 x 48 cm.)
Provenance: Jeanne Fevre, private collection; Paul Brame
Exhibitions: Amsterdam 1952, no. 29; Bern 1951-52, no. 36
Literature: Lemoisne 796bis

PAUL BRAME, PARIS

111 YOUNG WOMAN IN BLUE 1882-85

VENTE II: 163 VENTE stamp
LEMOISNE 782
Pastel
18½ x 12¼ in. (47 x 31 cm.)
Provenance: Vente Atelier Degas II, December 11-13, 1918, no. 163; Barthélémy, Paris

110

111

Literature: Lemoisne 782

112 THE CONVERSATION *(La Causerie)* 1882-85

VENTE I: 140 VENTE stamp l.l.
LEMOISNE 712
Pastel on tan paper
27½ x 27⁹⁄₁₆ in. (69.7 x 69.8 cm.)
Provenance: Vente Atelier Degas I, May 6-8,
1918, no. 140; Seligmann; Durand-Ruel;
Harry L. Bradley; his gift 1957
Exhibitions: Los Angeles 1958, no. 46
Literature: G. Bazin, *L'Amour de l'Art*, July
1931, p. 309; Lemoisne 712

MILWAUKEE ART CENTER
Gift of Harry Lynde Bradley
Shown only at The Minneapolis Institute
of Arts

113-114 *The Normandy house of his friend Paul
Valpinçon was always a place of relaxation
for Degas. Even during the fall of 1884,
when he was complaining about a bust he
claimed the family had shamed him into
making of their daughter Hortense, he wrote
(LETTRES pp. 92-93) about a comedy Hortense
and three friends had produced and acted at
Ménil-Hubert which had inspired him to
write a gallant sonnet. Something of the
character of his life there appears in later
photographs of Degas happily acting out a
melodrama with Hortense, her husband, and
presumably her brother in front of the
château itself (see Daniel Halévy,* My Friend
Degas, *trans. and ed. by Mina Curtiss,
Middletown: Wesleyan University Press,
opposite p. 80), Ménil-Hubert provided
solace for Degas after the Franco-Prussian
War. It was probably the place where he had
made his first drawings and paintings of
horses from life. He was bound to it by the
closest ties of nostalgia and affection which
were focused at times on the daughter of the
house, Hortense.*

*Degas had painted Hortense enchantingly
as a small child in the work (LEMOISNE 206)
which is now in the Minneapolis Institute
of Arts. He clearly wanted to do her justice
as an adult and embarked upon the ill-fated
bust the year before she married Jacques
Fourchy. It was at that time that he wrote*

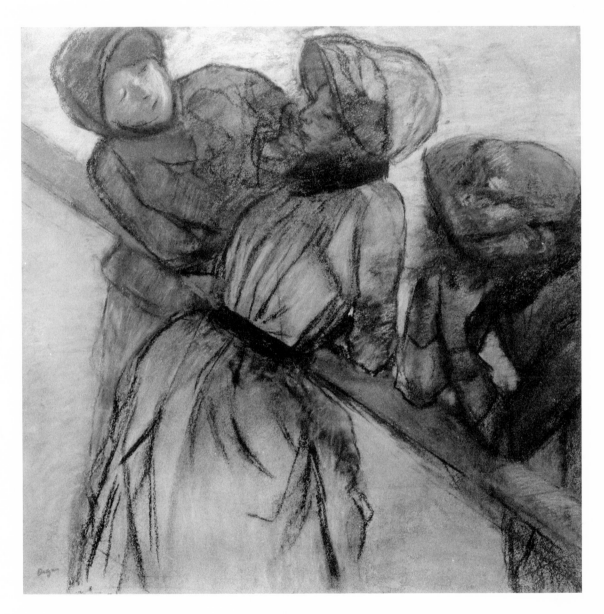

112

(LETTRES p. 90) that Hortense and a friend talked of nothing but marriage from dawn to dusk.

The two drawings in the exhibition were made the year before, 1883, and seem to symbolize Hortense's maturity, her hair now gathered with dignity on the top of her head. Their absolute departure from Degas's other portrait drawings of the time, which were conceived like nos. 108 and 110 from ingenious angles in space, show their importance. The cameo-like profile portrait (which does not, however, ignore the faint mole on Hortense's cheek), with its strong classical contours which continue round the head, is as inevitably unified as a Roman gem or Renaissance medal. Degas used the pastel and charcoal so that Hortense's hair is wonderfully soft, breaking into wisps in front of her ears and at the nape of her neck, and so that her skin has a faint bloom, more delicate than that of any 18th century pastellist. It is an unaffected compliment to Hortense and to the Valpinçon family. While Degas kept the pastel he gave the larger conté crayon drawing to Hortense's husband, Jacques Fourchy, presumably at the time of their marriage in 1885. It is believed that this is the first occasion the drawings have been reunited in an exhibition.

113

113 HORTENSE VALPINCON 1883

Conté crayon on white paper
13 x 10¾ in. (33 x 27.3 cm.)
Inscription: "Hortense / Ménil-Hubert / août 1883" l.r.
Provenance: Jacques Fourchy (husband of Hortense Valpinçon), Paris
Exhibitions: New York, Metropolitan Museum of Art, 1960 (June-September), *The Walter C. Baker Collection of Drawings*
Literature: Claus Virch, *Master Drawings in the Collection of Walter C. Baker*, New York: Metropolitan Museum of Art, 1962, no. 104

WALTER C. BAKER, NEW YORK

114 HORTENSE VALPINCON 1883

VENTE IV: 73b   VENTE stamp l.l.
LEMOISNE 722
Pastel

114

11⅜ x 6¼ in. (29 x 16 cm.)
Provenance: Vente Atelier Degas IV, July
2-4, 1919, no. 73b; Nunès et Fiquet;
Marcel Guérin
Exhibitions: Paris 1955, no. 15
Literature: Rivière no. 30; *L'Amour de l'Art,*
July 1931, p. 286; Lettres pl. VIII; Lemoisne
722; Boggs no. 125, p. 69

GUILLAUME GUERIN, SANARY-SUR-MER,
VAR, FRANCE

115-117 *About 1885 Degas made three pastels of a
trio of dancers performing. All three wore
the traditional ballet costume, with
particularly generous gauze skirts or tutus,
blue bodices, slightly ruffled and very
decolleté white blouses, with bows over
their shoulders. Their hair was built up at
the back, and heavy bangs covered their
foreheads. In one of these Degas showed the
dancers standing as if about to acknowledge
the audience's applause* (LEMOISNE 602), *in
another dropping into a very low curtsy*
(LEMOISNE 612), *in a third performing an
arabesque seen from the box of an
indifferent spectator* (LEMOISNE 586). *The
suggestion of the personality of the dancers
and their awkwardness destroys the illusion
of an idyllically smooth performance as if
they were illustrating what Degas described
in one of his sonnets as the leap of a frog
in the pools of Cythera.*

*The three drawings in the exhibition are
related to these pastels—although not to
any specific figure. The first (no. 115) in the
Lousada collection, with its precise pencil
touched up with white on pink paper,
suggests drawings of ballerinas a decade
earlier, but comparison with another dancer
adjusting her shoe from 1874 (no. 71)
makes it clear how much harsher in
conception this is—the body bonier, the
position starker, the lines severer.
Below her the head of the dancer is
transformed with a cap and bow into a
Pierrot, which tempts one to identify her
with the dancer Sanlaville who had
some success at pantomime and in assuming
male roles in the ballet versions of the
Commedia dell'Arte* (BROWSE pp. 57-58).

*The Hartford version seems to have
developed from a group of even freer
drawings of a dancer dropping into a curtsy,*

115

drawings which were probably made from life and about which Degas would make comments as he did on the one bowing, "Much too low / the legs are too far forward." At the stage of the Hartford work Degas emphasized the limbs, and the strain on them, by emphatic and highly articulating black lines. The pattern of the leg, the two arms and even the third arm, studied above, produce a rhythm which draws the dancer up and pushes her down again. The diamond-shaped grid for transferral suggests that Degas was aware of this rhythm although at the same time it also shows how much each part of the body departs from rigid geometry.

For the other pastel of the same dancer in the same position Degas used a piece of paper the same size but brought the dancer closer to the spectator and cut through her body at the median line of the Hartford drawing. There were other changes—he made the skirt more bouffant and increased the sense of space and light with the color of the pastel—but the essential change in emphasis seems to be upon the long arm, the delicate gesture of the hand, and the delighted absorption of the dancer. Her face is not young, and it is tempting to see in it again the dancer Sanlaville to whom Degas dedicated a sonnet in which he spoke of her art in which her "body moves eloquently and without noise," (LEMOISNE I, pp. 210-211).

115 DANCER ADJUSTING SLIPPER C. 1885

VENTE IV: 205a VENTE stamp l.l.
Pencil, touched with white, on pink paper
15¾ x 12¼ in. (40 x 31 cm.)
Related Material: VENTE II: 350; III: 86 (2)
Provenance: Vente Atelier Degas IV, July 2-4, 1919, no. 205a; Nunès et Fiquet
Exhibitions: London, Tate, 1926

ANTHONY LOUSADA, LONDON

116 BALLET DANCER CURTSYING C. 1885

VENTE III: 367(2) VENTE stamp l.l.
LEMOISNE 616bis
Charcoal and pastel on smooth, gray paper
18 x 12¼ in. (46 x 31 cm.)
Related Material: a) VENTE III: 86(1); IV: 286d; III: 137(2); III: 121(3); II: 233(2); b) LEMOISNE 602, 701, 586; c) 603, 604, 612

116

117

Provenance: Vente Atelier Degas III, April 7-9, 1919, no. 367(2); Durand-Ruel; Mrs. Cornelius Sullivan, New York; purchased from Mrs. Sullivan 1934
Exhibitions: Cambridge 1957
Literature: Walter Mehring, *Degas,* New York: Herrmann, 1944, no. 22; Rouart 1948, no. 9; Lemoisne no. 616bis; Browse no. 65; Roger-Marx no. pp.; Huttinger p. 65; Bouret p. 252
WADSWORTH ATHENEUM, HARTFORD 34.293
The Ella Gallup Sumner and Mary Catlin Sumner Collection

117 BALLET DANCER CURTSYING C. 1885

LEMOISNE 616
Pastel
18⅞ x 12¼ in. (46 x 31 cm.)
Provenance: Durand-Ruel; English Collection (Sale May 29, 1929, no. 26); Kojanovicz collection; Fritz Nathan (1954)
Literature: Lemoisne 616; Longstreet
MR. AND MRS. SYDNEY M. SHOENBERG, ST. LOUIS
Shown only at City Art Museum of Saint Louis

118-120 *From her knowledge of the dance Miss Browse has given the best analysis of the drawings from the eighties of dancers learning their job. They were young and fiercely attentive rather than endearing. Degas studied their movements with the same realism with which, inspired by Muybridge, he was studying the actions of horses and jockeys; they are, as a result, graceless but convincing. His criticism of the dancers in writing on the drawings is as trenchant as the drawings themselves, a pungent analysis of the actual effort involved in learning the dance. Only at moments does a certain tenderness arise, as it does in the small dancer (no. 120) with the conventional long pink bloomers under her white tutu who grabs one foot as she limbers up with some unknown exercise at the bar.*

118 DANCER AT THE BAR C. 1885

VENTE II: 215 (2) VENTE stamp l.l.
Charcoal with pastel on smooth cream paper
12¼ x 9 in. (31 x 23 cm.)
Inscription: "mauvais / le corps tourné / jambe gauche moins allongée / sur la

120

118

barre" l.l.
Provenance: Vente Atelier Degas II,
December 11-13, 1918, no. 215 (2)
Literature: Browse no. 151

MR. AND MRS. MICHAEL H. EGNAL, PHILADELPHIA

119 DANCER EXERCISING AT THE BAR C. 1885

VENTE III: 125 (4) VENTE stamp l.l.
Charcoal with pastel
11½ x 9 in. (30 x 23 cm.)
Inscription: "porter le corps sur la jambe
à terre"
Provenance: Vente Atelier Degas III, April
7-9, 1919, no. 125 (4); Durand-Ruel;
purchased by the Cincinnati Art Museum
1920
Literature: Browse no. 149

CINCINNATI ART MUSEUM

120 DANCER AT THE BAR C. 1885

VENTE II: 215 (1) VENTE stamp l.l.
Charcoal with pastel on smooth cream paper
12 x 9 in. (31 x 23 cm.)
Provenance: Vente Atelier Degas II,
December 11-13, 1918, no. 215 (1)
Literature: Browse no. 152

MR. AND MRS. SYDNEY M. SHOENBERG, ST. LOUIS
Shown only at City Art Museum of
Saint Louis

121 DANCER PREPARING FOR A PIROUETTE C. 1885

VENTE III: 119(2) VENTE stamp l.l.
Pencil on white, cold-pressed paper
9¹³⁄₁₆ x 12¾ in. (23 x 30 cm.)
Inscription: "préparation pour une
pirouette" u.l.; "bras mauvais" u.r.; "trop
large" l.c.
Provenance: Vente Atelier Degas III, April
7-9, 1919, no. 119(2); Durand-Ruel; gift of
Wright Ludington to Santa Barbara
Museum of Art
Exhibitions: Santa Barbara Museum of Art,
1955 (April 21-May 17), *Drawings of Five
Centuries,* no. 77; Eugene 1963, no. 8
Literature: Browse no. 127

SANTA BARBARA MUSEUM OF ART
Gift of Wright Ludington

This drawing, like nos. 118-120, analyzes
the dancer's imperfections. Miss Browse
points out that the right arm is, as Degas

119

121

wrote, bad because the elbow has not been raised as high as the hand. The dancer's rather clownish effect may also be explained by his comment that the space between her legs is too wide. We are left impressed with the drawing's boldness and the clumsy effort of the unknown ballerina.

122 DANCER DRAWING ON HER TIGHTS 1885-90

Study for LEMOISNE 941
Charcoal and pastel on yellowed paper
12⅛ x 15¼ in. (30.7 x 38.9 cm.)
Inscription: "Degas" l.r.
Related Works: L. 884bis; VENTE II: 217(2), 218(2); VENTE III: 109(4), 112(4), 138(4), 148(2), 248; VENTE IV: 160, 270b
Provenance: Max Liebermann, Berlin
Literature: Cooper no. 26

DR. FRITZ NATHAN AND DR. PETER NATHAN, ZURICH

In Degas's paintings of ballet classes two figures appear as stock characters to balance the activity of dancers exercising at the bar in the background; they rest on a bench, one pulling up her tights, as this dancer does, the other usually leaning over to tie the ribbons of her shoe. Degas drew this small dancer almost cryptically, but with a tenderness for the bent oval head and a pleasure in the contours of the uplifted leg. The lines Degas drew in order to transfer the drawing are not echoed in the finished work.

123-124 *About 1886 Degas drew and made pastels of ballerinas playing both the male and female roles in the ballet in the first act of* Les Jumeaux de Bergame. *One of them* (LEMOISNE 818) *is dedicated "à mon amie Hortense," and Lemoisne records it as having been given to her at the time of her marriage in 1885. It is possible that the gift may have been somewhat delayed and the series inspired, as Miss Browse suggests* (BROWSE p. 58), *by a gala performance of this ballet at the Opéra on January 26, 1886 in which Sanlaville (see nos. 115-117 and 127) danced Harlequin Senior and Mme Subra, Coraline or Colombine. Although both Miss Browse and Lemoisne date other versions of the subject much later (see* LEMOISNE 1111-1113, *c. 1891-95, and* BROWSE *no. 253, c. 1905-12) and there is admittedly*

122

no reason Degas would not have worked on this subject at a later time, these drawings are not sufficiently inconsistent to be far from 1886.

In the first version in the exhibition, no. 123, the two figures seem undressed—not nude but in the leotards dancers wear in rehearsal today. Colombine's right arm, which we see at the left, is comparatively lightly drawn, but over the contours of the rest Degas has pressed his charcoal down so heavily that we begin to see the drawing as an abstraction rather than as a record of a dance. It is an abstraction with puzzling dramatic overtones in the very richness of the black and the brutality of the strokes. The other version (no. 124) is more conventionally dressed, its lines more refined, the strength of the charcoal relieved by pastel; its spirit is more light-hearted and even flirtatious. Possibly Degas meant the undressing of the first version to be symbolic—an exposure of stronger human passions. He was still conceiving his figures sufficiently sculpturally to draw this same couple at least twice from the back.

123 DANCERS AS HARLEQUIN AND COLOMBINE
c. 1886

VENTE III: 265 VENTE stamp l.l.
Study for LEMOISNE 1111-1113
Charcoal on yellow paper
14⅛ x 11¾ in. (36 x 30 cm.)
Inscription: "rajouter 4e à gauche / 2e à droite / 3e en bas" u.r.
Related Works: VENTE IV: 263b; III: 179; IV: 155; II: 340
Provenance: Vente Atelier Degas III, April 7-9, 1919, no. 265; Nunès et Fiquet; F. Koenigs; given by D. G. van Beuningen 1940
Exhibitions: Rotterdam, Boymans, 1933-34, *Teekeningen van Ingres tot Seurat,* no. 52; Basel, Kunsthalle, 1935, no. 156; Amsterdam 1946, no. 67; Paris, Bibliothèque Nationale, 1952 (Feb. 20-April 20), *Dessins du XVᵉ au XIXᵉ siècle, Musée Boymans de Rotterdam,* no. 136
Literature: Longstreet

MUSEUM BOYMANS-VAN BEUNINGEN, ROTTERDAM
F II.217
Gift of D. G. van Beuningen

123

124

DANCERS AS HARLEQUIN AND COLOMBINE
c. 1886

VENTE III: 323 VENTE stamp l.l.
Charcoal with pastel
14½ x 12⅝ in. (37 x 32 cm.)
Provenance: Vente Atelier Degas III, *April
7-9, 1919, no. 323; Bernheim-Jeune*

DR. HERMANN J. ABS, FRANKFURT

125-126 *Hélène Rouart was, like Hortense Valpinçon
(see nos. 113 and 114), the daughter of an
old and close friend of the painter, Henri
Rouart. Earlier Degas painted her as a child
seeking protection on her father's knee
(LEMOISNE 424). There must have been a
fundamental difference between the two
girls because whereas the face of Hortense
Valpinçon in her childhood portrait
(LEMOISNE 206) is beautiful and serene,
Hélène Rouart's is shadowed and troubled.
The year after making the profile portraits of
Hortense, Degas, perhaps out of a sense of
loyalty and certainly out of a sense of
affection for the Rouarts', decided to work
toward a composition of Hélène with her
mother. The result was like the undressing of
Harlequin and Colombine (see no. 123)—
the exposure of feelings Degas didn't want
to admit to himself, let alone to the Rouarts.*

*If Degas dated the drawing in the Los
Angeles County Museum correctly (no.
125), two years later, when he decided to
make a portrait of Hélène, he must have
thought of the earlier composition and
dressed her, as he had then, in an enveloping
shawl which in the 1884 composition echoed
the shape of a tanagra figurine on a table
before Hélène and her mother. Degas
worked over the drawing in charcoal again
and again, gradually strengthening it with a
few bold strokes, and with pastel which
produced a diffusely melancholy atmosphere
around Hélène, very much like the
expression on her face.*

*Degas persisted in working toward a more
idyllic portrait, finally settling on
contemporary dress which freed her body
and gave it more animation. She now sat
casually on the arm of a chair in her father's
house, a more spirited position for a young
woman. The drawing in the exhibition (no.
126), which seems to follow a drawing in
the Bibliothèque Nationale in Paris (BN 6,*

125

126

*p. 204) and a pastel (LEMOISNE 871), is a
gesture toward greater vitality. The face is
only briefly indicated and inevitably not
flattering—but in the next version (LEMOISNE
870) Hélène is beautiful and dignified, and,
finally in the large painting which shows her
standing behind the chair, surrounded by
the collection of her father's house, she has
become worthy of her environment, even if
her classic face is still veiled with sadness.*

125 HELENE ROUART 1886

VENTE II: 329
LEMOISNE 866
Charcoal and pastel on tan paper
19¼ x 12½ in. (48.5 x 31.8 cm.)
Inscription: "Degas / 1886" l.r.
Provenance: Vente Atelier Degas II,
December 11-13, 1918, no. 329; Durand-
Ruel; Bernheim-Jeune; Mr. and Mrs.
Preston Harrison Collection
Exhibitions: Santa Barbara Museum of Art,
1956; Los Angeles 1958, no. 53; Minneapolis
and New York 1962, no. 30
Literature: Lemoisne 866; Jean S. Boggs,
"Mme Henri Rouart and Hélène by Edgar
Degas," *Bulletin of the Art Division,* Los
Angeles County Museum, no. 8, Spring
1956, pp. 13-17; Longstreet
LOS ANGELES COUNTY MUSEUM OF ART
*Mr. and Mrs. William Preston Harrison
Collection*

126 PORTRAIT OF HELENE ROUART 1886

VENTE II: 170 LEMOISNE 870bis
Study for L. 870
Pastel on matt, pale blue paper
19¼ x 13⅜ in. (49 x 34 cm.)
Inscription: "Degas / 1886" l.r.
Provenance: Vente Atelier Degas II,
December 11-13, 1918, no. 170; Ernest
Rouart, de Touraou and Jean Planque
collections
Exhibitions: London, 1963, Leicester
Galleries, *Artists as Collectors,* no. 112
Literature: Lemoisne, no. 870bis
MR. AND MRS. ELIOT HODGKIN, LONDON

127 MLLE S. *(première danseuse à l'Opéra)* 1887

VENTE II: 248 VENTE stamp
LEMOISNE 898

127

128

Charcoal with pastel

14³⁄₁₆ x 10¼ in. (39 x 27 cm.)

Provenance: Vente Atelier Degas II,
December 11-13, 1918, no. 248; Dr. Georges
Viau; Franz Koenigs

Exhibitions: Paris 1931, no. 127; Paris,
Seligmann, 1933, *Pastels français*, no. 73;
Amsterdam 1938, no. 46; Amsterdam 1946,
no. 71; Amsterdam 1952, no. 36;
Washington etc., 1952-3, *French Drawings*,
no. 156; Paris & Amsterdam 1964, no. 187,
pl. 145

Literature: Lemoisne 898; Browse no. 39a;
Boggs no. 130, p. 65

MME A. K. M. BOERLAGE-KOENIGS, LAREN,
THE NETHERLANDS

Perhaps because of his studies of the dance,
Degas became aware of the expressive
possibilities of feet, even with the long skirts
of the nineteenth century. The black boots
appearing under the skirt of Hélène Rouart
(no. 126) convey her fundamental
listlessness. In this portrait drawing, Degas
added a piece of paper for the outspread,
apparently ungainly boots which in their
unexpected position reveal the habits of the
former dancer. The limp, shapeless clothes,
the clownish position and the cruelly sharp
and thin features of the woman bring the
drawing close to devastating caricature,
which is avoided only by Mlle S.'s innate
dignity. Traditionally she has been known as
Mlle S ... première danseuse à l'Opéra, a
title which would apply to Rita Sangalli who
was thirty-eight in 1887. On the other hand
her position could have been less exalted,
and she might be Mlle Sanlaville (see nos.
115-117 and 123-124).

128 PORTRAIT OF A YOUNG WOMAN C. 1885

VENTE II: 127 VENTE stamp l.r.

LEMOISNE 802

Pastel

19 x 12 in. (49.5 x 32 cm.)

Provenance: Vente Atelier Degas II,
December 11-13, 1918, no. 127; Durand-
Ruel; Thannhauser, Lucerne

Exhibitions: Munich, Thannhauser
Gallery, 1926 (July), *Degas*, no. 10; Museum
of Fine Arts, Houston; Dallas Museum for
Contemporary Arts, 1961 (March 9-April 2);
*Impressionists and their Forebears from
Barbizon*, no. 38

129

Literature: Lemoisne 802, Boggs no. 117, pp. 63-64

OVETA CULP HOBBY, HOUSTON

Degas occasionally made unaffectedly dignified and pretty portraits of women conveying a sense of their inner dignity without losing their essential prettiness, much like the portraits of the eighteenth-century pastellists, Perronneau and Quentin de la Tour. The simple, almond-shaped head in this portrait with its strong features is a solid foundation for the feminine softness of the hair, the light on the skin, the dreamy eyes and the mobile mouth.

129 STANDING DANCER 1885-90

VENTE II: 174 VENTE stamp l.l.
LEMOISNE 901
Study for LEMOISNE 894
Pastel on gray paper
18⅝ x 11¾ in. (47.2 x 29.8 cm.)
Related Drawings: VENTE II: 218 (1), 220 (1); VENTE III: 376; Art Institute of Chicago 33.1230
Provenance: Vente Atelier Degas II, December 11-13, 1918, no. 174; Jaudé collection, Paris; Mrs. Gustav Radeke; her gift to the museum 1923
Literature: Lemoisne no. 901; Browse no. 194

MUSEUM OF ART, RHODE ISLAND SCHOOL OF DESIGN, PROVIDENCE 23.038
Gift of Mrs. Gustav Radeke

Degas must have decided to use charcoal and pastel on tinted paper for drawings of dancers to give them a greater luminosity as studies for the atmosphere-enveloped paintings of their classes. This is one of a group of such spontaneous drawings, worked out in perspective as if we are looking down from some height. Degas seems to have carried this drawing further by reinforcing the contours, particularly sculpturally in the arms, and by giving some indication of the setting in the shadows. Although the dancer sketched in on the right does not appear in the finished work, the shadows do. It is interesting to look back at the drawing of another dancer (no. 74) which is not so different in subject and technique; by comparison the Rhode Island School of Design pastel is a brutally

130

sculptural work, almost melodramatic in the force with which it was executed.

130 DANCER: *Danseuse vue de face, le bras gauche levé* c. 1890

VENTE II: 175 VENTE stamp l.l.
LEMOISNE 910
Pastel on gray paper
18 x 11½ in. (47.5 x 30 cm.)
Provenance: Vente Atelier Degas II,
December 11-13, 1918, no. 175; René de
Gas; Collection of a Gentleman (Sale,
Sotheby's, November 25, 1959, no. 54 to
Knoedler)
Exhibitions: Paris, Charpentier, 1943 (May-
June), *Scènes et figures parisiennes,* no. 67
Literature: Lafond, vol. II; Lemoisne no. 910
PRIVATE COLLECTION, NEW YORK

The latent melodrama in no. 129 comes to the surface in this pastel drawing where light and dark play against each other, dramatizing the anguish of the dancer who stretches one arm upward and puts the other to her forehead in pain. Degas has drawn the head as a sculptor, pressing his fingers under her brows to create the deep shadows there, distending her nostrils and goudging a hollow for her mouth; it has all the suggestion of agony of Rodin's head of Pierre de Wiessant for the *Burghers of Calais* which one might feel could have inspired it. The color and the light of this pastel are so hauntingly beautiful that they intensify the sense of pain.

131 NUDE DRYING HERSELF 1882-86

VENTE III: 347 VENTE stamp l.l.
Study for LEMOISNE 890
Pencil, heightened with white on rough,
discolored gray paper
17 x 11 in. (43.3 x 28 cm.)
Provenance: Vente Atelier Degas III, April
7-9, 1919, no. 347; Nunès et Fiquet;
purchased 1942
Literature: University of Oxford, *Report of
the Visitors of the Ashmolean Museum,*
1942, p. 22
VISITORS OF THE ASHMOLEAN MUSEUM, OXFORD

This drawing is a study for a pastel of a nude Claude Monet acquired. Because the setting parallels those for other nudes

131

134

133 BATHER C. 1883

VENTE III: 135(3) VENTE stamp l.l.
Study for LEMOISNE 717
Charcoal, heightened with white, on light
beige paper
12¼ x 9 in. (31 x 23 cm.)
Related Drawings: VENTE II: 222(2); VENTE
III: 110(2), 135(1), 142(4)
Provenance: Vente Atelier Degas III, April
7-9, 1919, no. 135(3)
Literature: Rouart, 1948, cover

CHARLES DURAND-RUEL, PARIS

Degas wanted the same spontaneity and
naturalness in his nudes as in his ballerinas
and jockeys. Instead of using classical poses
he asked his models to go through the
movements of their baths, and he even set
up zinc tubs for that purpose in his studio.
One action that attracted him was the
model's lifting her left knee to sponge it.
It required the kind of concentrated physical
purpose that appealed to him in the dance
and the race track. He studied it several
times; this is one of the early drawings but
it has been strengthened by the heavy,
broken lines of black charcoal and given a
glow by the use of the estompe and white
chalk underneath. The quick zigzagging
lines above the knee emphasize the action.

134 BATHER C. 1890

VENTE III: 348 VENTE stamp l.r.
Study for LEMOISNE 1028
Charcoal on white paper
23½ x 18 in. (60 x 46 cm.)
Counter-proof: VENTE IV: 366
Provenance: Vente Atelier Degas III, April
7-9, 1919, no. 348
Literature: Huttinger p. 50; Claude Roger-
Marx, *Degas, Pastels et Dessins,* Paris:
D. Jacomet, 1957

CHARLES DURAND-RUEL, PARIS

This nude stepping into a tub reveals, in
comparison with no. 133, how much more
complicated Degas's nudes had become.
Degas has exaggerated the perspective
drawing so that we seem to hover over the
figure and even to be thrust with her across
the tub. The arms of the nude straddle the
tub, and we can feel the pressure that the
weight of the leg puts upon them. The
contours of her body are thrust at different,

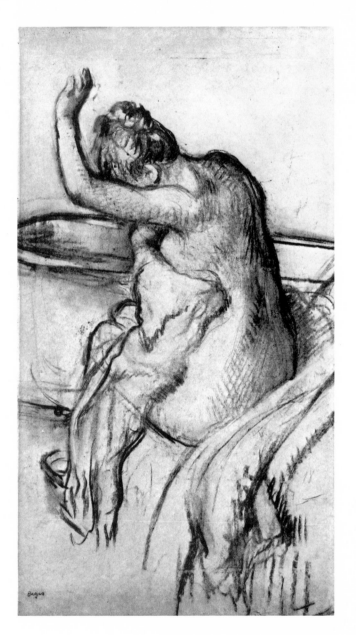

135

136

conflicting angles and vary in breadth, some dissolving into shadows. In this nude we are made aware of the physical strain of an athletically vigorous body rather than of flesh or skin.

135   AFTER THE BATH   c. 1890

VENTE II: 269   VENTE stamp l.l.
Study for LEMOISNE 1011
Charcoal on tracing paper, mounted on card
25⅞ x 14¾ in. (65.8 x 37 cm.)
Related Works: VENTE II: 293, 309, 311, 266;
VENTE I: 314
Impression: VENTE IV: 365
Provenance: Vente Atelier Degas II,
December 11-13, 1918, no. 269; Vollard;
Tanner; Collection Dr. Eduard Freiherr von
der Heydt, Ascona; his gift to the von der
Heydt Museum 1955
Exhibitions: Venice 1948, *Biennale XXIV,*
no. 72
*Literature: Verzeichnis der Hanzeichnungen
Pastelle und Aquarelle,* 1965, no. 43
VON DER HEYDT MUSEUM, WUPPERTAL

Degas's quieter nudes can be infinitely touching as this one is, sitting by her bath and drying under her breast. One of the reasons for this sense of pathos may be the improbability of her pose, the strained and needless lifting of her arm. Although the strokes of Degas's charcoal, seemingly affected by the technique he had evolved for hatching in pastels, weave in and out in contradiction to the texture of flesh, they do produce a luminous impression; even the shadows have their animation. And in the hair the strokes of the pastel suddenly become caressing. The tracing paper indicates that Degas had put it through several stages, working toward the final pastel.

136   LE PETIT DEJEUNER   c. 1890

VENTE I: 317   VENTE stamp l.l.
LEMOISNE 725
Study for LEMOISNE 724
Charcoal and brown chalk
37 x 23 in. (94 x 38.4 cm.)
Provenance: Vente Atelier Degas I, May 6-8,
1918, no. 317; A. Vollard; Jacques
Seligmann (his sale, American Art
Association, New York, January 27, 1921,

137

138

no. 1, to Reinhardt); Maurice Exsteens
Literature: Lemoisne no. 725

MR. AND MRS. T. M. STERLING, TORONTO

Degas's nudes normally seem vulnerable because we do not see their faces. But Degas also studied more self-sufficient figures like the maid-servant who carries a cup of chocolate to her mistress who is drying herself after a bath. This woman, who carefully watches the cup she is balancing in her hand, is dignified, even monumental, in spite of her nudity. Actually the pastel-like hatching of Degas's charcoal protects her body, and we concentrate upon her magnificent head and outstretched arm.

137 THE BATHER 1890-95

LEMOISNE 837
Charcoal and pastel
25 ½ x 19 in. (62 x 43 cm.)
Inscription: "Degas" l.r.
Related Study: VENTE III: 282
Related Works: LEMOISNE 1077, 1097, 1098
Provenance: A. Vollard, Paris; Galerie de l'Elysée, Paris
Exhibitions: Paris, Bernheim-Jeune, 1954, *Le Nu à travers les âges*, no. 12
Literature: A. Vollard, *98 Reproductions signées par Degas*, Paris: Vollard, 1914, pl. 59; Lemoisne no. 837

MR. AND MRS. GERARD L. ZOMBER; MASTERS
MICHAEL AND PETER ZOMBER,
ROSEMONT, PENNSYLVANIA

This nude at first seems to be from Degas's first series of bathers (for example L. 816, dated 1884) but it is far more forthright. The emphasis is not so much upon the tensions within the body as on the solid form of the projecting buttocks, fully and roundly described in strong charcoal and pastel. The unequivocal force of its conception and of its realization make it the kind of work which appealed to the dealer Ambroise Vollard who once owned it.

138 AFTER THE BATH C. 1895

VENTE I: 237 VENTE stamp u.l.
LEMOISNE 1232
Pastel
14 ⅜ x 13 in. (39 x 33 cm.)
Related Drawing: VENTE III: 175(2)

139

Provenance: Vente Atelier Degas I, May 6-8, 1918, no. 237; Comiot Collection
Exhibitions: Paris 1937, no. 174; Copenhagen, Ny Carlsberg Glypotek, 1948, *Degas*, no. 120; Bern 1952, no. 112
Literature: Vingt Dessins no. 19; F. Fosca, "La Collection Comiot," *L'Amour de l'Art*, April 1927, p. 112; Lemoisne no. 1232

OTTO WERTHEIMER, PARIS

About 1895 Degas did some of his most beautiful oil paintings of nudes, their colors strangely exotic as if they were an anticipation of the later work of Pierre Bonnard. The exoticism of the color was often quite independent of any literal description of a human figure in an interior. In the same way other elements of Degas's work became increasingly arbitrary and abstract. In this drawing, for example, Degas used the charcoal and pastel as though they were abrasive tools, their rough hatching creating an atmosphere of friction around the body which is twisted into an unlikely, if not ungraceful, position, caught between agony and ecstasy.

139-141 *Degas made many versions of a nude crouching on the side of a tub, drying her ankles; there is even one dated 1903 (LEMOISNE 1421) in Sao Paulo. Degas must have felt challenged to see what variations he could work out with this pose, largely by varying the space around each nude and by changing the character of the shadows on her body. There are three in the exhibition.*

Color alone makes the Josten version tender and sympathetic; in addition, the hair stays in a disciplined knot on the back of her head and her arms are appealingly articulated, thrust out at an angle as she dries her feet. The pressures within the body are indicated by shadows, lightly on her rump, more strongly on her breasts and still darker on her arms, as if they were drawn into the blackest area—the towel.

The black charcoal drawing on yellow tracing paper from Stuttgart is by far the most energetic and robust. The shadows reinforce the movements of the bather's body, in the arm, for example, without burdening them. Our eyes are carried up through the arm, down the spine and the buttocks into the leg in a movement which

140

*is boldly arched and uninterrupted, as
vigorous as her tossed hair and actively
crumpled towel.*

*In the third drawing, from the Zacks
collection, strong hatching lights the body
so that it seems more spectacularly
illuminated than the others. The bather's
unconfined long hair falls dramatically and
wetly downward, its movement reflected in
the liquid folds of the towel. The body itself
has become massive and its efforts therefore
heroic as if the weight of the flesh itself had
become an intolerable burden. Degas added
a piece of paper to the drawing to increase
the size of the room so that the mass of that
body would seem less oppressive against the
staccato but decorative strokes of red chalk
which surround it.*

139 AFTER THE BATH C. 1900

VENTE II: 203 VENTE stamp l.l.
LEMOISNE 1384
Pastel
18⅛ x 22⅞ in. (46 x 58 cm.)
Related Works: LEMOISNE 1380; 1383;
VENTE II: 291
Provenance: Vente Atelier Degas II,
December 11-13, 1918, no. 203; A. Vollard;
Galerie Charpentier, Paris, June 5, 1956,
no. 4
Literature: Lemoisne no. 1384

MRS. WERNER E. JOSTEN, NEW YORK

140 AFTER THE BATH C. 1900

VENTE II: 315 VENTE stamp l.l.
Charcoal on tracing paper, mounted on card
15¾ x 21¼ in. (40 x 54 cm.)
Provenance: Vente Atelier Degas II,
December 11-13, 1918, no. 315; Galerie
Thannhauser, Munich and Lucerne
Exhibitions: Munich, Galerie Thannhauser,
1926 (July), *Edgar Degas,* no. 19; Zurich,
Galerie Aktuaryus, 1935, *Degas,* no. 22
Literature: Johann Eckart v. Borries,
Zeichnungen des 19. und 20. Jahrhunderts,
Staatsgalerie Stuttgart, 1960, p. 16, no. 33

STAATSGALERIE STUTTGART: GRAPHISCHE
SAMMLUNG C50/161

141 AFTER THE BATH C. 1900

VENTE II: 67 VENTE stamp l.r.

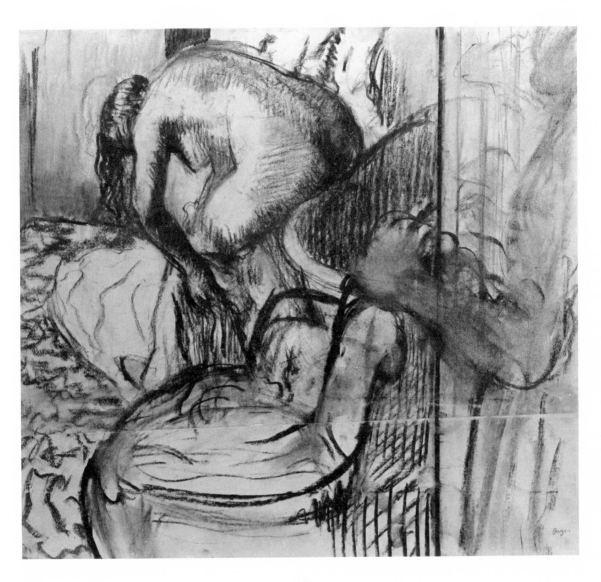

141

LEMOISNE 1382
Charcoal and pastel
22 x 23¾ in. (55 x 62 cm.)
Provenance: Vente Atelier Degas II,
December 11-13, 1918, no. 67; Pellet

AYALA AND SAM ZACKS COLLECTION, TORONTO

142-144   *Degas's fascination with women's fashion*
never deserted him. In the large pastel of
The Conversation *(no. 143), which he dated*
1895, he obviously delighted in the
enormous, feathered hats and leg-of-mutton
sleeves of contemporary dress. The decolleté
neckline of the yellow dress of the woman in
no. 142 is also described with considerable
precision. Even in 1905, in the quick drawing
of Mme Rouart (no. 144), he noted the
softening of the puffed sleeves and the
loosening of the bodice, blousing out at
the waist.

Degas continued to keep a sense of rhythm
moving through the whole body, through
the arms and head, and even the dress. This
rhythm, although not always as lethargic as
that in the portrait of the woman in yellow
is nevertheless slower, more continuous and
more ponderous than in his earlier work.
If we look back from the 1895 Conversation
to the Minneapolis version (no. 112), at
least a decade earlier, we discover how much
sprightlier the earlier work is.

This movement which seems to struggle
against a terrible inertia is an expression of
Degas's own deepening pessimism which he
often managed to conceal in the very
brilliance of the colours of the pastel as he
did in the Seated Woman in Yellow *and*
The Conversation *and in the final version of*
Mme Rouart with her Children *(LEMOISNE*
1450) for which no. 144 is a study. For the
Seated Woman in Yellow *there is a drawing*
(VENTE III: 302) which is as harsh, as crabby
and as tragically revealing as the
magnificently expressive charcoal of Mme
Rouart (no. 144). Here we find Degas rawly
conveying the inevitability, the ugliness and
the futility of the struggle of human life.

142   A SEATED WOMAN IN YELLOW   C. 1892-95

VENTE I: 253   VENTE stamp l.l.
LEMOISNE 1135
Pastel

142

28⅜ x 23⅝ in. (71 x 58 cm.)
Provenance: Vente Atelier Degas I, May 6-8,
1918, no. 253; Danthon collection, Paris
Exhibitions: New York 1958, no. 13, pl. VIII,
Baltimore 1962, no. 52, p. 55; New York
1960, no. 58
Literature: Denis Rouart, *Degas à la
recherche de sa technique*, Paris, 1945, p. 33;
Lemoisne no. 1135; Boggs no. 138

MR. AND MRS. LEO M. ROGERS, NEW YORK

143 THE CONVERSATION 1895

LEMOISNE 1175
Pastel on buff paper, laid on board
24¾ x 24 in. (65 x 61 cm.)
Inscription: "Degas / 95" l.r.
Provenance: Durand-Ruel; Wildenstein,
London; Sir Alexander Korda (sold
Sotheby's, London, June 14, 1962, no. 19)
Exhibitions: Paris, Musée des Arts
Décoratifs, 1933, *Le Décor de la Vie sous
la IIIe République*, no. 368; London, Agnew,
1936, *Degas*, no. 30
Literature: Lafond, vol. I, p. 72; C. Mauclair,
Degas, Paris: Hyperion, 1937, p. 63;
Lemoisne no. 1175

THE JOAN AND LESTER AVNET COLLECTION,
NEW YORK

144 PORTRAIT OF MME ALEXIS ROUART C. 1905

VENTE III: 303 VENTE stamp l.l.
Study for LEMOISNE 1450
Charcoal with pastel
24 x 18¼ in. (60 x 46 cm.)
Provenance: Vente Atelier Degas III, April
7-9, 1919, no. 303; Durand-Ruel;
Nierendorf Galleries, New York
Literature: Boggs no. 145

COLONEL SAMUEL A. BERGER, NEW YORK

145-147 *When we peel our way underneath the
dazzling colors of Degas's late paintings and
pastels of dancers, we finally reach the
barest bones—his studies of those dancers
nude. Their nudity is even less sensual and
idyllic than those of his bathers—partly
because their very athleticism seems to
destroy such possibilities. They are active,
even when they sit, in positions which
involve an exaggerated strain. He used
shadow, both inside and outside the*

143

contours of their bodies, to emphasize the conflicting pressures. Although in drawings no. 146 and 147 he did, at least, permit a varied and sweeping movement through the dancers' figures, he also used the charcoal brusquely so that the effect is one of energy rather than grace. The most poignant of these three drawings is the young dancer with the haggard face (no. 145) struggling so desperately to keep her foot on the bar. The lack of proportion between her effort and her achievement does not amuse Degas as it would have done in the past; he is both more sympathetically involved in her effort and critical of its necessity.

These preparatory studies, along with tracings and counter-proofs, were used to work toward the final composition. Lemoisne (LEMOISNE 515 bis) points out the difficulty in distinguishing the original drawing from an impression of it, which Degas might have touched up with pastel. It is possible, for example, that a counter-proof was taken from no. 147, removing a great deal of the surface of the charcoal, to use as the basis for the reversed, colored drawing of the same figure (LEMOISNE 1260). On the other hand, Degas may have taken an impression from another of his charcoal drawings as the basis for no. 145 which he would then have strengthened with more charcoal and pastel.

145 NUDE STUDY OF A DANCER C. 1900

LEMOISNE 182
Study for LEMOISNE 807
Charcoal and pastel
Related Drawings: VENTE III: 199; L. 1220
Provenance: A. Vollard; Jonas
Literature: A. Vollard, *98 Reproductions signées par Degas*, Paris: Vollard, 1914, pl. 73; Jamot pl. 73; Lemoisne no. 812
MR. AND MRS. LAWRENCE S. POLLOCK, DALLAS
Shown only at City Art Museum of
Saint Louis

146 NUDE STUDY OF A DANCER RESTING

c. 1895-1900
VENTE III: 236 VENTE stamp l.l.
Study for LEMOISNE 1326
Charcoal on white paper
26 x 18⅞ in. (66 x 48 cm.)

144

146

Related Drawing: VENTE III: 390
Provenance: Vente Atelier Degas III, April
7-9, 1919, no. 236
CHARLES DURAND-RUEL, PARIS

147 SEATED DANCER NUDE 1895-1900

VENTE IV: 297 VENTE stamp l.l.
Study for LEMOISNE 1260, 1260 bis
Charcoal
24½ x 19 in. (65 x 51 cm.)
Related Study: VENTE III: 275
Provenance: Vente Atelier Degas IV, July
2-4, 1919, no. 297; Knoedler, Chicago
Exhibitions: City Art Museum of St. Louis,
1961, *A Galaxy of Treasures from St. Louis
Collections*
Literature: City Art Museum Bulletin,
St. Louis, 1961, no. 4
MRS. LOUIS WERNER II, ST. LOUIS

148-150 *As an old man Degas seems to have been
haunted by the spectacle of the ballet—the
great operatic stage, the dancers grouped,
often behind richly colored flats, as they
prepared for the performance itself. In the
finished pastels and oils he used colors of
the most exotic intensity, and behind their
dazzling effects were drawings of the
austerity and power of nos. 148 and 149.*

*In these compositions Degas tended to mass
the dancers so that, as in no. 148, they
seemed to share a single torso and to have as
many complicating arms as Siva, the Indian
god who was sometimes associated with the
dance. Actually each arm can be logically
explained, even in its gesture. These
drawings are so compactly organized that in
the Oberlin drawing (no. 148) the left
dancer's right arm and shoulder strap lead
us into the neckline of the dancer in the
foreground, and the arm on the left begins a
diagonal which is continued in the raised
arm at the back. One might expect a conflict
between such classical control and the
emotionalism of the jagged strokes of
charcoal and almost abrasive hatching, but
Degas's compulsive sense of rhythm,
in the movement through the arms and
bodice of the front dancer, seems to provide
their reconciliation.*

*No. 149 is one of several drawings leading to
no. 150 and, with it, to the most developed*

145

147

pastel (LEMOISNE 1342). It was not unusual for Degas to have made the strong charcoal drawing of the dancers nude, even when their principal gestures are concerned with the adjustment of their non-existent clothing. In the Logan drawing (no. 150) those gestures are retained but made more feminine. The movements through the bodies, which in the other version are curvilinear, have become sprightlier and more angular. Flowers have been added to lighten the downward pull of the hair. The face of the upper dancer has been redrawn so that her eyebrows and her mouth wing upward with more animation. Finally Degas added the touches of color—the blue, the violet and the glowing golden red he adored in hair—so that the work sparkles with the vivacity he wanted to remember in the dance.

148 A GROUP OF DANCERS C. 1900

VENTE III: 221 VENTE stamp l.l.
Study for LEMOISNE 1416
Charcoal on manila-toned paper, pasted on cardboard
28 x 19½ in. (73 x 51 cm.)
Provenance: Vente Atelier Degas III,
April 7-9, 1919, no. 221; René de Gas; Marie Harriman Gallery
Exhibitions: New York, Museum of Modern Art, 1944 (February 16-May 31), *Modern Drawings*, p. 90; New York, Knoedler, 1954 (February 3-21), *Paintings and Drawings from Five Centuries*, no. 64; Ann Arbor, University of Michigan Museum, 1956 (March 11-April 1), *Drawings and Watercolors from the Oberlin Collection*; Los Angeles 1958, no. 69; Milwaukee Art Center, 1960 (October 20-December 4), *Men at Work—Daumier to Shahn*
Literature: Allen Memorial Art Museum Bulletin: I, no. 2, 1944, no. 103, p. 41; XI, no. 2, 1954, no. 64; XXI, no. 2, Winter 1964, p. 81, no. 11, p. 82

ALLEN MEMORIAL ART MUSEUM,
OBERLIN COLLEGE

149 FOUR DANCERS C. 1900

VENTE I: 335 VENTE stamp l.l.
LEMOISNE 1357
Study for LEMOISNE 1352
Charcoal with pastel

148

32 x 22 in. (81 x 56 cm.)
Provenance: Vente Atelier Degas I, May 6-8,
1918, no. 335; Berry collection, Paris;
Mrs. John W. Garrett
Exhibitions: Baltimore 1962, no. 65, ill. p. 39
Literature: LEMOISNE no. 1357

THE EVERGREEN HOUSE FOUNDATION, BALTIMORE

150 STUDIES OF BALLET DANCERS *(half-length)*

c. 1900
VENTE I: 217 VENTE stamp l.l.
LEMOISNE 1354
Study for LEMOISNE 1352
Charcoal and pastel
27½ x 28¼ in. (72 x 70 cm.)
Provenance: Vente Atelier Degas I, May 6-8,
1918, no. 217; A. Vollard; Jacques
Seligmann, Paris (Sale, American Art
Association, New York, Januray 27, 1921,
no. 4); Durand-Ruel; A. Vollard, Paris
Exhibitions: New York 1958, no. 28
Literature: C. Mauclair, *Degas*, Paris:
Hyperion, 1937, p. 132; Lemoisne no. 1354;
Browse no. 241; Moskowitz & Mongan,
no. 792

MR. AND MRS. JOSHUA LOGAN, NEW YORK

151-153 *Degas continued to use his charcoal as if he
were modeling with clay, giving his contours
extraordinarily sculptural force as they
describe, for example, the standing ballerina
leaning against a wall (no. 151). He even
seemed to hollow out space, as he did
between the two resting ballerinas in
drawing no. 152. At the same time he gave
these drawings something sculpture could
not possess—a sense of light. His strokes of
charcoal, so harsh and so rough, vary from
the velvety shadow down the shoulder blade
of the standing dancer, the undulating
waves of her hair, the coarse cross-hatching
on the wall, to passages of unbroken white,
like the upper surface of her right arm; these
vibrate enough to suggest the unreal
theatrical light of a gas-lit stage.*

*In looking at these drawings it is easy to
think of them as abstractions of light and
shadow and strong, dynamic line. But even
if the dancers do not possess the refined
articulation of his earlier work, those
abstract qualities are intended as description.
In the Boston drawing (no. 153) the force*

149

150

which builds up with line and light and shadow toward the upper left of the drawing is propelling the dancers across the stage (as we can see in the large oil painting in the National Gallery in Washington for which this was a study). The basic difference between these and earlier works is not so much in the degree of abstraction but in the movement which here seems the result of a compulsion rather than of individual desire.

151 BALLET DANCER RESTING C. 1900

VENTE II: 274 VENTE stamp l.l.
ATELIER stamp *verso*
Study for LEMOISNE 942, 945, 1066
Charcoal on cream cardboard
19⁹⁄₁₆ x 12¼ in. (50 x 31 cm.)
Counter-proof: VENTE II: 384
Provenance: Vente Atelier Degas II,
December 11-13, 1918, no. 274; A. Vollard;
Wright Ludington gift to the Santa Barbara
Museum of Art
Exhibitions: La Jolla Art Center, 1955 and
1960; Los Angeles 1958, no. 58; Baltimore
1962, no. 66, ill. p. 38; Eugene, 1963 no. 9;
Los Angeles, University of California, 1964
Literature: Browse no. 209

SANTA BARBARA MUSEUM OF ART
Gift of Wright Ludington

152 TWO DANCERS IN REPOSE C. 1890-1900

VENTE II: 288 VENTE stamp l.l.
Study for LEMOISNE 1101
Charcoal with pastel
21⅜ x 18⅞ in. (53 x 48 cm.)
Provenance: Vente Atelier Degas II,
December 11-13, 1918, no. 288;
Durand-Ruel; Louis E. Stern, New York
Exhibitions: Brooklyn 1962-63, Brooklyn
Museum of Art, *The Louis E. Stern
Collection,* no. 112
Literature: Philadelphia Museum of Art,
The Louis E. Stern Collection, 1964, no. 57,
ill. p. 55

PHILADELPHIA MUSEUM OF ART
The Louis E. Stern Collection

153 THREE DANCERS C. 1890

VENTE II: 335 VENTE stamp l.l.
Study for LEMOISNE 987
Charcoal and pastel on blue-gray paper

151

152

23^{13}/$_{16}$ x 18^{1}/$_{8}$ in. (61 x 47 cm.)
Provenance: Vente Atelier Degas II,
December 11-13, 1918, no. 335; John T.
Spaulding; his bequest June 3, 1948
Exhibitions: Boston 1935, no. 116; Boston,
Museum of Fine Arts, 1935, no. 116; Boston,
The Collection of John Taylor Spaulding,
no. 92a, plate VIII; Cambridge 1957; New
York 1958, no. 41, pl. XXX
Literature: Browse no. 189

MUSEUM OF FINE ARTS, BOSTON 48.872
Bequest of John T. Spaulding

154-155   *Degas's confidence in the individual, which
had been so fundamental in his earlier
works, even in his gently mocking portraits
of Diego Martelli (no. 88) or Mlle S...
(no. 127), disappeared toward the end of his
life. He now began to see human beings as
caught up, or even trapped, in activities they
could not determine. One vehicle to
express this was the dance, and one of the
most effective of these the wild movements
of a group of Russian peasants, so vigorous
and so compelling that no single ballerina
could escape. Since the dancers in the
charcoal and red chalk drawings are like
wraiths, it is interesting to look back some
thirty years earlier to those ghostly nuns
who performed in the ballet in* Robert le
Diable *(nos. 63, 64). The comparison makes
us realize how violently active and
interdependent these Russian dancers are.
In pastel (no. 155) we can see how Degas
heightened the wildness of the effect with
the intensity of the color and the vibrancy of
the strokes of pastel.*

*These Russian dancers are so thrilling that
no one has been content to leave them
unexplained. Lemoisne (*LEMOISNE 1181*)
believes them to be a troupe of Russian
dancers who performed in their national
costume at the* Folies-Bergères *in 1895. Miss
Browse (*BROWSE 242*) sees them as dancing
the Hopak from* Le Festin *staged by
Diaghilev's company when it first visited
Paris in 1909. The owner of both these
drawings suggests it is from* Boris Godunov.
*The quality of the line in the charcoal and
chalk drawings is like that of* Mme Rouart
*(no. 144), which we know to be from 1905,
so that this late date is not impossible.*

153

154 RUSSIAN DANCERS C. 1895-1905

VENTE III: 286 VENTE stamp l.l.
Study for LEMOISNE 1190
Charcoal with red chalk on buff paper
39½ x 30 in. (99 x 75 cm.)
Provenance: Vente Atelier Degas III, *April
7-9, 1919, no. 286;* A. Vollard; Mme de
Galea, Paris

MR. AND MRS. ALEX M. LEWYT, NEW YORK

155 RUSSIAN DANCERS C. 1895-1905

VENTE I: 270 VENTE stamp l.l.
LEMOISNE 1187
Pastel
23 x 30 in. (57 x 75 cm.)
Provenance: Vente Atelier Degas I, *May 6-8,
1918, no. 270; Vente Succession de René
de Gas,* Hotel Drouot, Paris, November 10,
1927, no. 38; Diéterle collection, Paris;
Albert S. Henraux collection, Paris
Exhibitions: New York 1960, no. 64
Literature: Lemoisne no. 1187

MR. AND MRS. ALEX M. LEWYT, NEW YORK

156 DANCERS ON THE STAGE C. 1905

VENTE III: 60
LEMOISNE 1461
Study for LEMOISNE 1459
Charcoal and pastel
22⅜ x 23¾ in. (57 x 63 cm.)
Provenance: Vente Atelier Degas III, *April
7-9, 1919, no. 60;* Durand-Ruel; Knoedler,
Paris; Mrs. John H. Winterbotham
Literature: Lemoisne no. 1461; Browse
no. 255

THEODORA W. BROWN AND RUE W. SHAW,
CHICAGO

Degas's dancers aged with him and, in doing
so, reflected his general pessimism at the
beginning of the twentieth century. Their
frail bodies lost substance and became
tremulous spirits. This charcoal has a rather
anxious intensity in the foreground where
the three dancers meet and talk to each
other, but the dancers in the background are
a flutter of red chalk. All seem ghosts of the
memories Degas was trying to summon
up from the past.

154

156

ABBREVIATIONS

ATELIER stamp — "ATELIER ED. DEGAS," contained within an oval, stamped in black on the contents of his studio after his death. See Frits Lugt, *Les Marques de Collections de Dessins et d'Estampes*, Amsterdam: Drukkerijen, 1921, p. 117, no. 657

BN — Reference to twenty-eight notebooks by Degas in the Bibliothèque Nationale, Paris. They are in the Réserves of the Cabinet des Estampes and are numbered Carnet D.C. 327.

DELTEIL — Loys Delteil, *Le Peintre-graveur illustré*, vol. IX: *Edgar Degas*, Paris: author, 1919

LEMOISNE — P. A. Lemoisne, *Degas et son oeuvre*, 4 vols., Paris: Brame & de Hauke, 1947-49

VENTE I — *Vente Atelier Degas*, Galerie George Petit, Paris, May 6-8, 1918

VENTE II — *Vente Atelier Degas*, Galerie George Petit, Paris, December 11-13, 1918

VENTE III — *Vente Atelier Degas*, Galerie George Petit, Paris, April 7-9, 1919

VENTE IV — *Vente Atelier Degas*, Galerie George Petit, Paris, July 2-4, 1919

VENTE V — A sale projected but not held. Photographs of works intended for it are in the archives of Durand-Ruel. There is a possible confusion between these and drawings grouped under a number in the VENTE I

VENTE stamp — "Degas," as if it were a signature, stamped in red on most of the drawings sold in the Ventes (see above). The same stamp was sometimes used with black ink for impressions but occasionally by error on the first version. See Lugt, *op. cit.*, p. 117, no. 658

Literature

BOGGS — Jean S. Boggs, *Portrait by Degas*, Berkeley and Los Angeles: University of California Press, 1962

BOGGS — Jean S. Boggs, "Degas Notebooks at the Bibliothèque Nationale," *Burlington*, May, June, July 1958

BOGGS — Jean S. Boggs, "Edgar Degas and Naples," *Burlington* June 1963, pp. 273-276

BOURET — Jean Bouret, *Degas*, tr. by Daphne Woodward, London: Thames & Hudson, 1965

BROWSE — Lillian Browse, *Degas Dancers*, London: Faber & Faber, [1949]

CABANNE — Pierre Cabanne, *Edgar Degas*, Paris: Tisné, 1960

CHAMPIGNEULLE — Bernard Champigneulle, *Degas Dessins*, Paris: Editions des Deux Mondes, 1952

CLARK — *Drawings from the Clark Art Institute: a Catalogue Raisonné* by Egbert Haverkamp-Begemann, Standish D. Lawder and Charles W. Talbot Jr., New Haven: Yale University Press, 1964

COOPER — Douglas Cooper, *Pastels by Degas*, Basel: Holbein, [1952]

GRAPPE — Georges Grappe, "Degas et le théâtre," *L'illustration*, 1937, Noël

HALEVY — Daniel Halévy, *Album de Dessins de Degas*, Paris: Quatre Chemins-Editart, 1949

HUTTINGER — Edouard Hüttinger, *Degas*, trans. by Ellen Healy, New York: Crown Publishers, 1960

HUYGHE — Réne Huyghe, *Edgar-Hilaire-Germain Degas*, Paris: Flammarion, 1953

HUYGHE & JACCOTTET — René Huyghe and Philippe Jaccottet, *Le dessin français au XIXe siècle*, Lausanne: Mermod, 1948

JAMOT — Paul Jamot, *Degas*, Paris: Gazette des Beaux-Arts, 1924

LAFOND — Paul Lafond, *Degas*, 2 vols., Paris: H. Floury, 1918-19

LEMOISNE — Paul-André Lemoisne, *Degas et son oeuvre*, 4 vols., Paris: Paul Brame & C. M. de Hauke, 1947-49

LETTRES — *Lettres de Degas*, edited by Marcel Guérin, Paris: Grasset, 1945

LEYMARIE — Jean Leymarie, *Les Dessins de Degas*, Paris: Hazan, 1948

LONGSTREET — Stephen Longstreet, *The Drawings of Degas*, Los Angeles: Borden [1964] (no page nos.)

MONGAN — Agnes Mongan, "Portrait Studies by Degas in American Collections," *Bulletin of the Fogg Art Museum*, May 1932, vol. I: 61-8, pp. 64-65

MONGAN & SACHS — Agnes Mongan and Paul J. Sachs, *Drawings in the Fogg Museum of Art*, 3 vols., Cambridge: Harvard, 1940

MOSKOWITZ & MONGAN — Ira Moskowitz and Agnes Mongan, *Great Drawings of All Times*, Vol. III, New York, Shorewood [1962]

PECIRKA — Jaromir Pecírka, *Drawings of Edgar Degas*, London: Peter Nevill, 1963

REFF — Theodore Reff, "Degas's Copies of Older Art," *Burlington*, June 1963, pp. 241-251

REFF — Theodore Reff, "New Light on Degas's Copies," *Burlington*, June 1964, pp. 250-259

REFF — Theodore Reff, "Addenda on Degas's Copies," *Burlington*, June 1965, pp. 320-323

REFF — Theodore Reff, "The Chronology of Degas's Notebooks," *Burlington*, December 1965, pp. 606-616

REWALD — John Rewald, *The History of Impressionism*, New York: Museum of Modern Art, 1946

REWALD — John Rewald, *The History of Impressionism*, 2nd ed., New York: Museum of Modern Art, 1961

RIVIERE — Henri Rivière, *Les Dessins de Degas*, Paris: Demotte, 1922-23

ROGER-MARX — Claude Roger-Marx, *Degas Danseuses*, Paris: Hazan, 1956

ROSENBERG — Jakob Rosenberg, *Great Draughtsmen from Pisanello to Picasso*, Cambridge: Harvard, 1959

ROUART — Denis Rouart, *Degas Dessins*, Paris: Braun, 1948

SCHWABE — Randolph Schwabe, *Degas the Draughtsman*, London: Art Trade Press: 1948

SHOOLMAN & SLATKIN — Regina Shoolman and Charles E. Slatkin, *Six Centuries of French Master Drawings in America*, New York: Oxford, 1950

VINGT DESSINS — *Degas-Vingt Dessins*, 1861-96, Paris: Goupil & Co., and Boussod, Manzi, Joyant & Co. (n.d., by 1897)

WALKER — John Walker, "Degas et les maîtres anciens," *Gazette des Beaux-Arts*, September 1933, pp. 173-185

Exhibitions

AMSTERDAM 1938 — Paul Cassirer, *Fransche Meesters uit de XIXe eeuw*

AMSTERDAM 1946 — Stedelijk Museum, *Teekeningen van Fransche Meesters*

AMSTERDAM 1952 — Stedelijk Museum, *Edgar Degas*

AMSTERDAM 1964 — Rijksmuseum, *Le Dessin français dans les collections hollandaises*, June 25-August 16 (Paris, Institut Néerlandais, May 4-June 14)

BALTIMORE 1962 — The Baltimore Museum of Art, *Manet, Degas, Berthe Morisot, and Mary Cassatt*, April 18-June 3

BASEL 1935 — Kunsthalle, *Meisterzeichnungen französischer Künstler von Ingres bis Cézanne*

BERN 1951-52 — Kunstmuseum, *Degas*, November 25-January 13

BOSTON 1935 — Museum of Fine Arts, *Independent Painters of 19th Century Paris*, March 15-April 28

BROOKLYN 1939 — Brooklyn Institute of Arts and Sciences Museum

BUENOS AIRES 1934 — *Degas*

BUFFALO 1935 — Albright Art Gallery, *Master Drawings*, January

CAMBRIDGE 1929 — Fogg Art Museum, Harvard University, *Exhibition of French Painting of the Nineteenth and Twentieth Centuries*, March 6-April 6

CAMBRIDGE 1931 — Fogg Art Museum, *Degas*

CAMBRIDGE 1934 — Fogg Art Museum, *French Drawings and Paintings of the 19th Century*, March 13-May 8

CAMBRIDGE 1957 — Fogg Art Museum, *Degas Dancers*, February 14-March 16

CAMBRIDGE 1961 — Fogg Art Museum, *Ingres and Degas, Two Classical Draughtsmen*, April 24-May 20

CAMBRIDGE 1965-66 — Fogg Art Museum, *Memorial Exhibitions: Works of Art from the Collection of Paul J. Sachs*, November 11-January 15

CHICAGO 1955-56 — Art Institute of Chicago, *French Drawings*, organized by *L'Association française d'Action Artistique*, circulated by the Art Institute of Chicago to the Minneapolis Institute of Arts, Detroit Institute of Arts, California Palace of the Legion of Honor

CLEVELAND 1947 — The Cleveland Museum of Art, *Works by Edgar Degas*, February 5-March 9

COPENHAGEN 1948 — Ny Carlsberg Glyptotek, *Edgar Degas*, September 4-26

DETROIT 1941 — Detroit Institute of Arts, *Masterpieces of 19th and 20th Century French Drawings*, May 1-June 1

EUGENE 1963 — University of Oregon, *The Dance in Art*, February 19-April 7

LOS ANGELES 1958 — Los Angeles County Museum, *Edgar-Hilaire-Germain Degas*, March

MINNEAPOLIS 1948	Minneapolis Institute of Fine Arts, *Degas Portraits*, March 6-28 (no numbers)	NORTHAMPTON 1933	Smith College Museum of Art, *Edgar Degas*
MINNEAPOLIS 1962	University of Minnesota, *The Nineteenth Century: One Hundred and twenty-five Master Drawings*, March 26-April 23 (New York, Guggenheim, May 15-July 1)	PARIS 1924	Galerie George Petit, *Exposition Degas*, April 12-May 2
		PARIS 1931	Orangerie, *Degas Portraitiste Sculpteur*
		PARIS 1937	Orangerie, *Degas*, March and April
NEW ORLEANS 1965	Isaac Delgado Museum, *Edgar Degas: His Family and his friends in New Orleans*, May 2-June 16	PARIS 1955	Gazette des Beaux-Arts, *Degas dans les Collections françaises*
		PARIS 1955	Orangerie, *De David à Toulouse-Lautrec*
NEW YORK 1921	New York, American Art Association, *Private Collection of Paintings and Pastels by Degas formed by Jacques Seligmann, New York*, January 27	PARIS 1958-59	Orangerie, *French Drawings from American Collections, Clouet to Matisse* (see New York 1959 and Rotterdam)
NEW YORK 1930	Jacques Seligmann & Co., *Drawings by Degas*	PARIS 1960	Durand-Ruel, *Edgar Degas*, June 9-October 1
NEW YORK 1945	Buchholz Gallery, *Edgar Degas*, January 3-27	PARIS 1964	Cabinet des Dessins, Louvre, *Dessins sculpteurs de Pajou à Rodin*
NEW YORK 1947	Century Club, Loan Exhibition, February 19-April 10	PARIS 1964	Institut Néerlandais, *Le Dessin français dans les collections Hollandaises*, May 4-June 14 (see Amsterdam 1964)
NEW YORK 1949	Wildenstein, *Degas*, April 7-May 14	
NEW YORK 1958	Charles E. Slatkin Galleries, *Renoir, Degas*, November 7-December 6	PHILADELPHIA 1936	Philadelphia Museum of Art, *Degas*
		RICHMOND 1952	Virginia Museum of Fine Arts, *French Drawings from the Fogg Art Museum*, March & April
NEW YORK 1959	Metropolitan Museum of Art, *French Drawings from American Collections: Clouet to Matisse*, organized by the International Council of the Museum of Modern Art, February 3-March 15	ROTTERDAM 1933-34	Boymans, *Teekeningen van Ingres tot Seurat*
		ROTTERDAM 1958-59	Boymans, *French Drawings from American Collections, Clouet to Matisse* (see New York 1959 and Paris 1958
NEW YORK 1960	Wildenstein, *Degas*, April 7-May 7	SAN FRANCISCO 1947	California Palace of the Legion of Honor, *19th Century French Drawings*, March 8-April 6
NEW YORK 1962	Guggenheim, *The Nineteenth Century: One Hundred and twenty-five Master Drawings*, May 15-July 1 (see Minneapolis 1962)	ST. LOUIS 1932	City Art Museum, *Edgar Degas*
NEW YORK 1966-67	Museum of Modern Art, *Memorial Exhibition: Works of Art from the Collection of Paul J. Sachs* (see Cambridge 1965), December 19-February 26	WASHINGTON 1947	Phillips Memorial Gallery, *Loan Exhibition of Drawings and Pastels by Edgar Degas*, March 30-April 30

SELECTED READING LIST

CATALOGUES OF DEGAS'S WORKS

Lemoisne, Paul-André, *Degas et son oeuvre*, Paris: Brame et de Hauke, 4 vols., 1947-49

Ventes Atelier Degas, Galerie George Petit, Paris: Vente I, May 6-8, 1918; Vente II, December 11-13, 1918; Vente III, April 7-9, 1919; Vente IV, July 2-4, 1919

GENERAL MONOGRAPHS

Boggs, Jean S., *Portraits by Degas*, Berkeley and Los Angeles: University of California Press, 1962

Browse, Lillian, *Degas Dancers*, London: Faber & Faber [1947]

Cabanne, Pierre, *Edgar Degas*, Paris: Tisné, 1960

Jamot, Paul, *Degas*, Paris: Gazette des Beaux-Arts, 1924

Lafond, Paul, *Degas*, 2 vols., Paris: H. Floury, 1918-19

Pool, Phoebe, *Degas*, New York: Marboro, 1963

Valéry, Paul, *Degas Danse Dessin*, Paris: Vollard, 1936; Paris: Gallimard, 1938; *Degas Manet Morisot*, trans. by David, Paul, New York: Bollingen Series XLV: 12, 1960

STUDIES OF DEGAS'S TECHNIQUES

Chialiva, Jules, "Comment Degas a changé sa technique du dessin," *Bulletin de la Société de l'histoire de l'art français*, 1932

Rouart, Denis, *Degas à la récherche de sa technique*, Paris: Floury, 1945

BOOKS ON DEGAS'S DRAWINGS

Champigneulle, Bernard, *Degas Dessins*, Paris: Editions des Deux Mondes, 1952

Cooper, Douglas, *Pastels by Degas*, New York: British Book Centre, 1953

Degas-Vingt Dessins, 1861-96, Paris: Goupil & Co. and Boussod, Manzi, Joyant & Co., n.d. (1896-97)

Halévy, Daniel, *Album de Dessins de Degas*, Paris: Quatre Chemins-Editart, 1949

Leymarie, Jean, *Les Dessins de Degas*, Paris: Hazan, 1948 and 1953

Longstreet, Stephen, *The Drawings of Degas*, Los Angeles: Borden, 1964

Nicodemi, Giorgio, *Degas 28 Designi*, Milan, 1944

Pecírka, Jaromir, *Drawings of Edgar Degas*, London: Peter Nevill, 1963

Rivière, Henri, *Les Dessins de Degas*, Paris: Demotte, 1922-23

Rosenberg, Jakob, *Great Draughtsmen from Pisanello to Picasso*, Cambridge: Harvard, 1959

Rouart, Denis, *Degas Dessins*, Paris: Braun, 1948

Schwabe, R., *Degas the Draughtsman*, London, The Art Trade Press, 1948

SPECIALIZED STUDIES ON DRAWINGS

Boggs, Jean S., "Degas Notebooks in the Bibliothèque Nationale," *The Burlington Magazine*, May 1958, pp. 163-171; June 1958, pp. 196-205; July 1958, pp. 240-246

Fries, G., "Degas et les maîtres," *Art de France*, 1964, pp. 352-356

Reff, Theodore, "Degas's Copies of Older Art," *The Burlington Magazine*, June 1963, pp. 241-251; "New Light on Degas's Copies," *The Burlington Magazine*, June 1964, pp. 250-259; "Addenda on Degas's Copies," *The Burlington Magazine*, June 1965, pp. 320-323; "The Chronology of Degas's Notebooks," *The Burlington Magazine*, December 1965, pp. 606-616

CHRONOLOGY OF THE LIFE OF EDGAR DEGAS

1834   July 19, Hilaire-Germain-Edgar De Gas born at 8, rue Paris, eldest son of Neapolitan-born Augustin De Gas and New Orleans-born Célestine Musson De Gas

1838   brother Achille born in Paris

1840   sister Thérèse born in Naples

1842   sister Marguerite born in Paris

1845   brother René born in Paris. Edgar entered Lycée Louis-le-Grand where Henri Rouart, Paul Valpinçon and Ludovic Halévy were his friends

1847   mother died

1848   year of Revolutions. In Italy the eldest son of his Aunt Rosa Morbilli was killed, and the husband of his Aunt Laure Bellelli was exiled from Naples

1853   March 23, received his bachelier-ès-lettres; April 7 registered at the Louvre and on April 9 at the Bibliothèque Nationale as a pupil of Félix-Joseph Barrias in order to copy; November 12 began to study law at the Faculté de Droit.

1854   seems to have rebelled against his father, left the Faculté de Droit, studied with the painter Louis Lamothe, and lived apart from his family

1855   April 6, introduced to the Ecole des Beaux-Arts by Louis Lamothe; among his fellow students were Léon Bonnat, Elie Delaunay and Fantin-Latour. Through his friends the Valpinçons, whom he persuaded to lend their great *Bather* by Ingres to the *Exposition Universelle*, he met Ingres.

1856   Sometime after April went to Italy, presumably visiting the exiled Bellellis in Florence and certainly visiting his grandfather René-Hilaire Degas and his Morbilli aunt and cousins in Naples, but stayed in Rome. He seems to have worked in classes at the French Academy in Rome, the Villa Medici, perhaps taken there by his friend at the Ecole des Beaux-Arts in Paris, Elie Delaunay.

1857   Spent the year in Rome with a trip to his grandfather in Naples during the summer.

1858   First part of the year in Rome. From July 24 to August 4 he travelled from Rome to Florence. In September his grandfather died in Naples but he remained in Florence working toward his first major painting, *The Bellelli Family*. Met with the Italian artists know as the Macchiaioli at the Café Michelangiolo

1859   Returned from Italy to Paris in April, continued to work on the *Bellelli Family*, and made studies for the *Daughter of Jephthah*.

1860   Spent part of the year in Italy. Worked apparently simultaneously on three history paintings, *The Daughter of Jephthah*, which he was finished, *The Young Spartans*, and *Semiramis* which he was beginning.

1863   April 16, Thérèse Degas and Edmond Morbilli were married.

1863-65   Visit to France from New Orleans of three female members of the family of his Uncle Michel Musson, his Aunt Odile and his cousins Desirée and Estelle. Estelle's husband, David Balfour, had been killed during the Civil War. They stayed at Bourg-en-Bresse where the painter visited them.

1865   Degas's first exhibition at the Salon with the *Scène de guerre au moyen-âge* which seems to have aroused no interest except for a compliment from Puvis de Chavannes to the young painter. June 1, marriage of Marguerite De Gas to Henri Fevre, architect.

1865-70   Exhibited in the Salon, in 1865 for the first time, in 1870 for the last; in 1866 it was the *Scène de Steeple-Chase*. Became a close friend of Manet and part of the group of artists, Monet, Renoir, Berthe Morisot, Whistler, Fantin-Latour, Tissot, who saw a great deal of each other, often at the Café Guerbois.

1869   René De Gas married their blind, widowed cousin, Estelle Musson Balfour in New Orleans

1870   With the outbreak of the Franco-Prussian War in 1870 he went into the Artillery where he served under his school friend, Henri Rouart

1871   Recuperated from the war and stayed out the period of the Commune with his friends, the Valpinçons, at their house in Normandy.

1872   Actively made studies of dancing classes and rehearsals at the Opera House on the rue le Peletier; sold first works to Durand-Ruel; October, left for New Orleans with brother René to visit René's family, his other brother Achille and his Musson uncle and cousins in New Orleans.

1873   Left New Orleans probably in January. December, signed the "manifesto" which was to result in the first "Impressionist" exhibition and went to Turin where his father had become seriously ill.

1874   February 23, father died in Naples. April 15, opening of first exhibition of group to be known as Impressionists. Beginning of serious financial difficulties.

1875   Sold his collection of paintings to help the family avoid bankruptcy.

1876   April, Second Impressionist Exhibition. Father's estate was liquidated.

1877   Third Impressionist Exhibition.

1878   Sold first work to a museum, *The Cotton Market*, to Pau.

1879   Fourth Impressionist Exhibition: exhibited fans, *Mlle Lala*, portrait of Diego Martelli.

1880   Fifth Impressionist Exhibition.

1881   Sixth Impressionist Exhibition; exhibited *Small Dancer of Fourteen Years* in wax which he had intended to exhibit the year before; September 27 Muybridge's photographs were published in *Le Globe*.

1886   Exhibited in last of Impressionist exhibitions; included a group of ten nudes in pastel; signed a contract with Durand-Ruel.

1893   First one-man exhibition at Durand-Ruel; exhibited landscapes; death of brother Achille.

1895   Death of sister Marguerite in Buenos Aires.

1917   Died September 27 and buried in Montmartre Cemetery.